PIONEERS IN PRINTING

PIONEERS IN PRINTING

JOHANN GUTENBERG

WILLIAM CAXTON

WILLIAM CASLON

JOHN BASKERVILLE

ALOIS SENEFELDER

FREDERICK KOENIG

OTTMAR MERGENTHALER

TOLBERT LANSTON

by

SEÁN JENNETT

ROUTLEDGE & KEGAN PAUL LIMITED

68-74 CARTER LANE LONDON

First published in 1958
by Routledge & Kegan Paul Limited
Broadway House, 68–74 Carter Lane, London E.C.4
and printed in Great Britain
by Butler & Tanner Limited
Frome and London

PREFACE

IT is always surprising, when investigation is made, how little we really know of even the most famous figures. In the absence of diaries or extensive correspondence, there is little to go on even in the case of familiar and well-loved people whose names have become a coin of popular exchange and whose picture is clear in the mind. The most obvious example of this is, of course, William Shakespeare, of whom we know nothing of importance, whose very existence is denied by some, and his achievements by others, and whose face, seen in a million of books, rests more upon imagination than on the fact of contemporary portraits.

This is in more or less degree the case with many of the prominent figures in the history of printing, and is true of those I have dealt with here, with the exception of Senefelder, who wrote a book about his invention, and possibly of Mergenthaler. Gutenberg is as shadowy as Shakespeare, and has suffered the same sort of imputation—that he never existed, and that if he did, he has received credit for what was not his work; and yet there is enough on record to show, however vaguely, a powerful and active figure, of strong personality, and that is how the many purely imaginary portraits show him. It is not altogether the distance of time that is responsible for this effacement. The character and deeds of William Caxton are clearer to us than those of Tolbert Lanston, the inventor of the Monotype, who died in 1913. Caxton speaks through his prefaces in a voice which, despite the archaisms, we recognize as the voice of a homely and humane man, who might sit with us about the fire to talk of books and printing; but Lanston, only fifty years after his death, is no more than a cold wraith, as formless and invisible as the air that drives his machines.

These are some of the difficulties that beset the author writing about people. To bring life to these subjects, imagination is needed, and facts and events must be assumed for which there is no record, but which seem possible and likely in the context. I have done this frequently, and I make no apology for it; but I have tried to keep clear what is based on record—though the records themselves may be disputed, erroneous, and untrustworthy.

My purpose has been to present as people the men on whose achievements the following chapters are based.

ACKNOWLEDGEMENTS

I acknowledge with gratitude the loan of material for the illustrations in this book by the Cambridge University Press, the Henry E. Huntington Library, the Bodleian Library, the Linotype & Machinery Co. Ltd., Stephenson, Blake & Co. Ltd., and especially to St. Bride's Library, to whose librarian, Mr. Turner Berry, I am greatly indebted. The chapter on Baskerville has appeared as an article in *Printing Review*.

CONTENTS

PREFACE   *page* v

JOHANN GUTENBERG AND THE INVENTION
    OF PRINTING   I

WILLIAM CAXTON   28

WILLIAM CASLON   47

JOHN BASKERVILLE   59

SENEFELDER AND THE INVENTION OF LITHO-
    GRAPHY   91

THE PRINTING MACHINE AND FREDERICK
    KOENIG   106

THE ADVENT OF THE COMPOSING MACHINE   153

MERGENTHALER AND THE INVENTION OF
    THE LINOTYPE   163

TOLBERT LANSTON AND THE MONOTYPE   178

INDEX   193

ILLUSTRATIONS

1. Gutenberg *page* 4
2. Casting type in 1568 10
3. *The World Judgement*, the earliest example of printing from movable types 12
4. Indulgences printed in Mainz in 1454 18–19
5. An eighteenth-century type mould 22
6. A punch, a matrix, and cast type 23
7. Gutenberg's press 25
8. A pair of ink balls 26
9. Chess-players: a woodcut from one of Caxton's
   books 35
10. A reader in the fifteenth century 38
11. The sign of the Red Pale 39
12. Caxton's house in Westminster 40
13. Some types used by Caxton 42–3
14. Caxton's device 45
15. Caslon's specimen sheet of 1734 52–3
16. Caslon's foundry in 1750 55
17. John Baskerville 63
18. Baskerville's prospectus for his Virgil 68–9
19. Caslon's types compared with Baskerville's 72
20. A page from *Paradise Lost* 75
21. The title-page of the Bible published in 1763 83
22. The last page of Baskerville's will 86
23. Senefelder's first press 98
24. A lithographic stone 99
25. A more advanced press designed by Senefelder 100
26. A third Senefelder press 101
27. A bookbinder's press 107

ix

28. An early printing press, 1507   *page* 109
29. A heavier press   110
30. A hand-press free from attachment to the ceiling   111
31. An eighteenth-century wooden hand-press   112
32. The Stanhope press   113
33. The Columbian hand-press   114
34. The Albion hand-press   115
35. Koenig's Suhl machine   123
36. Koenig's first metal printing machine, 1810   128
37. The first cylinder printing machine, 1812   130
38. Koenig's double-feeder *Times* machine   133
39. Koenig's perfecting machine of 1816   137
40. Applegath and Cowper's four-feeder press   145
41. Hoe's 'Lightning' press   146
42. An early Wharfedale   148
43. The machine room of an American printing house about 1883   149
44. Gordon's Franklin platen machine   151
45. Composing room of the *Western Daily News* in 1874   154
46. Hattersley's typesetting machine   156
47. A Kastenbein typesetting machine   157
48. The machine room of the State printing house in Vienna about 1840   160
49. The Paige typesetting machine   161
50. A diagram of Mergenthaler's band machine   168
51. Mergenthaler demonstrating his 'Blower' machine   170
52. The 'Blower' Linotype   172
53. The operation of the Linotype   174
54. Lanston's first Monotype casting machine   182

PLATES

I. The 42-line Bible   *facing page* 16

II. The 36-line Bible   17

III. Caxton presenting a copy of the *Recuyell* to Lady Margaret, Duchess of Burgundy   32

IV. William Caslon   33

V. Birmingham in 1731   60

VI. Baskerville's house, Easy Hill   80

VII. Baskerville's punches   81

VIII. Alois Senefelder   96

IX. Ottmar Mergenthaler   97

X. The square-base Linotype, with a Linotype slug   164

XI. A modern Linotype   165

XII. A line of matrices, with space bands   165

XIII. Tolbert Lanston   172

XIV. The Monotype keyboard and caster in 1900   173

JOHANN GUTENBERG
AND THE INVENTION
OF PRINTING

SCHOLARS, antiquaries, and archivists have studied over and over again the scanty records of the early days of the invention of printing. They have searched laboriously through the libraries and archives of such towns as Strasburg and Mainz, Bamberg and Cologne, for documents that might add a detail to the story, or they have taken to pieces the bindings of old books to see if somewhere behind the leather or the vellum could be found a scrap of paper, mere waste in the binder's estimation, but treasure to the scholar, which would give a clue, or fix a date, or prove some point. Every researcher has hoped, however secretly, that he might one day light on incontrovertible evidence that would banish all doubt. There may once have been such documents. Who can say what irrecoverable evidence rose in flames to the sky when the citizens of Strasburg, in the revolutionary fervour of Napoleon's age, set fire in the squares to cartloads of cartularies and other documents? There is surely little left to find nowadays—unless, perhaps, it might be a document long known and of which a transcript exists, but of which the original was mislaid in some great library a century or half a century ago; for this has happened to several Gutenberg papers, and there are some that cannot be found still, though it is known that they existed, and where, and when copies were made. So what we have in the way of documentary evidence of the history of printing before the year 1450 would go into a very slender file. On the other hand, what we have in the way of controversy and exegesis based on these documents would cause storage problems for a librarian. And that is without the addition of all the rest of the paper put forth by the supporters of other, and in some cases highly unlikely, claimants to the invention.

Out of all the doubt and discussion emerges a shadowy yet strangely positive figure, the most likely inventor. He is Johann Gutenberg of Mainz, or Johann Gensfleisch, called Gutenberg, and also variously called in the records Hans, Henne, Henchin, Hengin, all these being variants of the name Johann. Gensfleisch was his family name; Gutenberg came from the name of the house once owned by his family, the Hof zum Gutenberg.

Johann Gutenberg was born, probably in Mainz, between 1394 and 1400, on the eve of the Renaissance, of which he was himself to secure the foundations and the achievements. The times were troubled, and often lawless; and the Great Schism and its quarrelling prelates did nothing towards peace. In Mainz the archbishop of one pope threatened and attacked the archbishop of the other pope, each struggling for the control of the see. Rome and Avignon fought for power before the eyes of the citizens of a German town. In addition, there was another constant source of dispute and faction, the contest between the patricians and the guilds for the control of the council of Mainz. It is therefore not surprising that there is no record of Gutenberg's birth, nor of the place of his birth, though it may be assumed that he called himself Gutenberg from his having been born in that house. His father was Friele Gensfleisch and his mother Friele's second wife Else Wirich. There was a daughter of the first marriage, Johann's stepsister Patze, who married in 1403. Johann was the youngest of three children of the second marriage, the others being Friele a brother and his sister Else. The Gensfleisch family was apparently of some importance in Mainz. Patze married Peter Blashoff, who was mayor of the town, while Else married a well connected young man, Claus Vitztum, who was to be of service to Gutenberg later. These marriages presumably could not have taken place if the family had not been sufficiently endowed to maintain a patrician status.

There is no record of Gutenberg's education, no record at all of the first twenty years of his life. He is mentioned in a document of 1420, when he took part in a dispute concerning the distribution of his father's estate. A great deal of what is known about Gutenberg comes from the records of disputes. In this case, it was between Friele, Henchen, and Claus Vitztum on one side against Patze on the other. A legal document was drawn up to settle the matter. Perhaps Patze, the child of the first marriage, felt herself in priority over the younger family of the second marriage. She does not come into the picture again, and it is likely that Gutenberg had little to do with this stepsister old enough to be his aunt, and who, married off when he was a child, could never have seemed to him like a sister.

Some other documents mention Gutenberg during the next four years, but they are formal and do nothing to enlighten the history of printing or to elucidate his character. In 1430, however, he is shown as absent from Mainz, apparently as an involuntary exile, and he, with others, is invited to return. The reasons for his exile are not known, but they were probably connected with one of the many factions or conflicts in the town. He evidently did not accept the invitation, for he is next heard of in Strasburg in 1434—though he may have been in Mainz the previous year, when his mother died and her estate was divided among the heirs. It could not have amounted to much, his share, for Gutenberg was never wealthy. His mother had been living on half of an annuity he possessed, which he had made over to her in 1430, which does not suggest that she had adequate means either. It does suggest that he was an affectionate son and that he might have made the journey to Mainz when she fell mortally ill. But he was no famous son returning to his native city. Now nearly forty, he had barely started, if at all, on the work which was to make him famous, if not in his own time, then to all posterity.

In 1434 he was definitely in Strasburg; and so too was the city clerk of Mainz, for Gutenberg seized him and had him

1. No contemporary portrait of Gutenberg exists. This picture, from an engraving published in Paris in 1584, shows features no doubt imaginary but now traditional—the flowing moustache, the forked beard, and the suggestion of a powerful frame. The right hand holds what may be intended for an engraving tool, and the left an object carrying part of the alphabet, perhaps a collection of punches.

imprisoned. Gutenberg contended that the city of Mainz owed him money, probably annuity payments, and he intended to hold the unfortunate clerk as a hostage until the money was paid.

This account is of great interest because it shows for the first time Gutenberg in action, and something of the character of the man; and it shows too that he was in need of money, for surely he would not otherwise so recklessly have risked the enmity of his native city. There is no contemporary portrait of Gutenberg, but later portraits show him as a large, muscular man with a forked beard and fierce expression. These representations must be imaginative, but perhaps there is a grain of truth in them. Certainly the forked beard does not ill become the man who appears so rarely from behind the documents. His seizure of the clerk suggests that he was, at times at least, impulsive and reckless, sometimes inconsiderate and overbearing. But he could be reasonable too, and sensible of his own advantage, for when the council of Strasburg intervened on behalf of the clerk, Gutenberg agreed to let him go and freed him from all the claims he had made against him—but without prejudice to his claims against Mainz.

Gutenberg's financial problems were eased soon afterwards, when his brother Friele transferred an annuity to him, a gesture no doubt intended to keep Johann out of trouble. The claims on Mainz were maintained, however, at first with no result, but a few years later the city's authorities paid some sums of money to Gutenberg on account of overdue annuities, and paid the annuity itself, for a time at least. The money was received on Gutenberg's behalf by Claus Vitztum, who had evidently stayed in Mainz in 1428, when others went into exile, or perhaps had returned in 1430.

However, if his finances were better, Gutenberg's personal affairs were becoming involved, for in 1436 he was called upon to defend himself in a breach of promise action. It was brought by a lady of the name of Ennelin zu der Iserin Thüre—Anna of the Iron Gate. Gutenberg did defend himself, with vigour, to such effect that a shoemaker appearing for Anna brought an action against Gutenberg for slander.

Gutenberg had described Schotten Lawel, the shoemaker, as a miserable wretch who lived by cheating and lying, and as much else that I would like to know, but which the account calls sedately 'much defamatory language'. Evidently Gutenberg himself was not at all sedate, and one may fancy the muscular bulk of the man, and the forked beard, and the fierce expression, and the contemptuous words. No wonder the poor shoemaker protested.

The slander action was heard during the progress of the breach of promise case, and Gutenberg was ordered to pay the shoemaker fifteen Rhenish gulden provisionally pending the end of the main case. What that end was is unfortunately not known. Most scholars believe that whatever Anna may have got, she did not get Gutenberg.

At this time Gutenberg was living outside the walls of Strasburg, but what he was doing is not clear. He is recorded in 1439 as having a large quantity of wine in his possession— nearly two thousand litres—on which he had to pay tax. This would appear to be the cellar only of a wealthy man or a wine merchant, but there is no evidence that Gutenberg was either of these. In this same year, however, there was yet another lawsuit, and the depositions of some of the witnesses, tantalizing in their half revealed and ambiguous technicalities, seem to show that Gutenberg was already interested in printing.

He had had more than one iron in the fire. He had worked out some process for polishing stones, presumably precious stones, and he took into partnership with him Hans Riffe, Andres Heilmann, and Andres Dritzehen. It was agreed that these three should be taught the method of the process, and for this privilege each of them would pay the inventor eighty gulden; which money was to be Gutenberg's entirely, and not an investment in the partnership. The venture prospered well enough to make the partners deeply interested when they discovered that Gutenberg had developed another secret process. They urged him to reveal it, and offered money for the knowledge. An agreement was reached by which the partners were to pay ninety gulden each on the same terms as before. The partnership was to last five years, and if any partner died during that period his heirs were not to inherit his share, but were to be satisfied by the payment of a hundred gulden in settlement of all claims. This condition was imposed so that there could be no necessity of divulging the secret to others.

What was this secret? There was some discussion during the trial of the manufacture of mirrors to be marketed during the pilgrimage to Aachen in 1439, but nothing was said that referred in any way to the practical technique of this business of mirror manufacture. There is no reference to the purchase of glass or mercury or whatever was used for mirrors in the fifteenth century, nor is it explained why pilgrims should have particular need of them. Of course, the pilgrimage was a great affair that brought crowds of people into the district, many of them in holiday mood and prepared to buy from the shops and stalls that would spring up along the way. No doubt there would be a sale for all kinds of shiny and tawdry stuff tricked out to take the eye. Even so, this manufacture of mirrors has a curious air of unreality. The pilgrimage did not take place until the following year. Could they be making the goods so far in advance? Or was the manufacture of mirrors a red herring, a device intended to conceal the real secret, a device intended to mislead and yet truthful enough to those who knew that there was double meaning? Obviously, none of the partners would want the secret, whatever it was, to be divulged in open court, and so a subterfuge would be natural. It has been suggested that these mirrors were not looking-glasses at all, but copies of a book called *Speculum Salutis*, or *The Mirror of Salvation*. This religious work had been popular in manuscript since the twelfth century, and it was later to be popular as a printed book. What could be more suitable for sale to pilgrims, particularly if copies could be produced at prices below those that had been common until now.

If there are no details in the evidence of the case that refer to looking-glasses, there are many references that can be understood, and are clear, if the reference is to printing. Hans Dunne, the goldsmith, said clearly that three years before he had earned a hundred gulden from Gutenberg solely for

7

what referred to printing. There is mention of presses, formes, lead, and of a mysterious instrument that would fall into pieces when two screws were loosened, and which would then be unrecognizable, whereas, assembled, it might have betrayed the secret. This instrument had been in the care of Andres Dritzehen at his house, where he had been working on it. When Andres died, Gutenberg, it is recorded, sent repeatedly to his house with instructions that the object should be dismantled at once, before anyone should recognize its purpose.

Whatever this object was, it was clearly the crux of the secret. Most people think of a printer as a man who works a printing press, and they imagine that the invention of printing was the invention of the printing press. That is an erroneous idea. There were many kinds of presses before Gutenberg was born, and many of them, with a little adaptation, would have served the purposes of a printer. It is not impossible that there were such presses in operation, printing images from wood blocks. Printing, with or without a press, was known in Gutenberg's day, and indeed had been known in his grandfather's day. The men who gambled with cards in a tavern were using the product of a printing process; and the pilgrim who carried with him the picture of a saint, perhaps as early as the twelfth century, had it by benefit of printing. Hans Dunne, the goldsmith, did not have to search for a newfangled word when he spoke of the work he did for Gutenberg: the word existed and was common coinage.

What then might this secret thing have been? It was certainly not a press, for it was described as being in or on a press. It could be taken from there by one man, so it must have been easily portable. It was very costly, also, as we shall see in a moment. And it was the heart of the secret. I do not think there is anything in printing that fits as well into this description as the mould, the instrument that forms the body of the piece of type, and at the same time contains the matrix, which forms the face, the letter itself. The inventor of printing as we know it, printing with separate characters of type, known as 'movable types', which can be assembled

8

into any form of words, and into pages of words, to print thousands of letters at one stroke, any such inventor must have made a mould to manufacture the types. He could not avoid it, for there is no other way in which it can be done. A mould is not a thing, like a press, that can be adapted from something else, or which can be constructed by accident by idle fingers, or discovered almost unintentionally, as the principle of lithography was to be discovered two hundred and fifty years later. It could only have been made by taking thought, and could only have been thought of by a man who had need of it to implement his conception.

Let us look at it from the point of view of the inventor. Perhaps he tried to make type, as has been suggested, by engraving letters on a wooden block and then cutting them apart as small sticks of wood each with a letter on the end. It can be done. But when he came to assemble the letters into words, how were they to be held together while the printing was done from them? They must stand shoulder to shoulder in straight lines in any conceivable combination, shoulder to shoulder, head to toe, throughout a page. Any trial would show that nothing rough and ready would do; *approximately* rectangular is not good enough. It is possible that previous inventors got as far as this, possible that that 'prefiguration' of printing in Holland mentioned by the *Cologne Chronicle* in 1499 was something of this kind. No such process could be successful. It would be borne in upon the inventor that the body or shank of every letter must be made rectangular with a high degree of precision, since type is added to type, and any error of dimension is therefore multiplied. No amount of wearisome fabrication with file and saw could achieve such precision so many times over. The only way to do it is to cast the characters in a common mould, so that their dimensions and rectangularity must agree. One of the side walls of the mould must be adjustable, however, since characters vary in width from an i to a w.

Gutenberg must have made moulds later in his life, otherwise he could not have produced type. I have no doubt that the thing that Andres Dritzehen had in his house was a type mould, for it had cost a lot of money, indeed, all of Andres'

9

money, and many hours of his time. Because it must be precise a type mould is an expensive thing even today, and when it had to be made by hand, and by experiment, it must have needed many hours of unremitting and painstaking work. Even a modern mould looks very little for what one must pay

2. This woodcut from Jost Amman's *Book of Trades* (1568) is the earliest representation of the casting of type. In his left hand the workman holds what is presumably a mould, though it is unlike surviving moulds from later periods; there are others on the shelf, inexplicably emitting smoke. With the ladle in his right hand he carries molten metal from the furnace before him and pours it into the mould. At his feet is a basket of types.

for it. Barbel, a neighbour of Andres, bustling in one day, and seeing him at work on the thing, remarked that it must have cost him a pretty penny, 'more than ten gulden, say'. Andres answered indignantly that it had cost him more than three hundred gulden, yes, nearer five hundred gulden, and it was like to cost him more yet. It was ruining him. But he hoped that before the year was out the thing would be done, and all his capital would come back to him then. Such is the optimism of inventors. That capital was never to return. Neither he, nor Hans Riffe, nor Andres Heilmann, nor Gutenberg himself, was destined to grow rich from printing. Not for another fifteen years was this new industry to begin to make anybody's fortune, and then it was not the fortune of the inventor, but that of those who had ruined him.

Andres died and the thing he had worked on could not be found—which shows incidentally that it could have been of no great size. His fortune and his inheritance were gone, and he had not completed the payment of the agreed fees to Gutenberg. His brothers began to sue Gutenberg for the return of the money which had been paid, or alternatively for a share in the partnership. The case came to court, and judgement was entered in Gutenberg's favour. The partnership agreement was clear. Gutenberg agreed to pay the hundred gulden due on a partner's death, but he was allowed to deduct from it the eighty-five gulden that Andres still owed him. The brothers therefore received fifteen gulden for their trouble.

Presumably the three remaining partners, Riffe, Heilmann, and Gutenberg, carried on, since the partnership agreement had originally been made out for five years. If so, the business, like many another business in its early days, eventually needed a transfusion of capital, for in 1442 Gutenberg borrowed eighty pounds—not a small sum—from St. Thomas's Chapter at Strasburg. Perhaps it was needed for the production of a book that is known now as *The World Judgement.* All we have of this book is a small fragment of paper with eleven lines of type on each side. It was found in Mainz in 1892. The type in which it is printed seems to be an early version of the type used a decade later in Mainz for the 31-line indulgences and the 36-line Bible. This is the earliest known example of printing with movable types.

In 1444 the partnership would have come to an end, according to the agreement, and the fact that Gutenberg's presence in Strasburg was not recorded after this year suggests that the agreement was not renewed. Riffe and

leben wil niuize ꝛo vien ꝛo got oꝛcri nui̇
gebē Sie gene mit ſchreckē ꝛobien Die
got nye erkante noch forchte eñ Niema
mag ſich ȯbergē nicht Vor dē gotlichē
angeſiecht Criſtus wil ꝛo urtel ſprechea·
Vñ wil alle boſzheit rechen Die nſe ge-
dadᷓ ꝛen willē iln Den wil er gebē ewige
pin Vñ wil ꝛen gudē gebē Hy vm freuꝛe
vñ ewig lebē Sſit die werlt vñ alle ꝺing
Die in ꝺ werlt geſchaffī ſint Czu gene
vñ werꝺē auch zu nicht Als man wol

3. These lines of *type* come from one side of a fragment of paper,
known as *The World Judgement*, discovered in Mainz in 1892, the
earliest example of printing from movable types. It was printed
about 1442. Even at this early period the type and the alinement
are good, which suggest that considerable experience had already
been gained.

Heilmann are not known to have continued printing. There is
no record of Gutenberg's movements until 1448, when he is
shown to have borrowed a hundred and fifty pounds at five
per cent in Mainz, a kinsman, Arnold Gelthius, standing
security for him.

A hundred and fifty pounds was a considerable sum of
money in the fifteenth century, when a man might work at
the plough for a week for a few shillings. There must have
been some large reason, some extensive project, to warrant
so large a loan. Gutenberg may already have been planning
the production of the 36-line Bible. A Bible is a formidable
proposition even for a modern printer, and the outlay in
type, ink, paper, and labour is very large. It is not probable
that any equipment Gutenberg may have brought from
Strasburg would be adequate for such a purpose. Like many
other inventors, Gutenberg was ready to borrow, and he had
a facility in borrowing that eventually was to bring him to
ruin. This loan of a hundred and fifty pounds was never to
be repaid, any more than the money borrowed from St.
Thomas's Chapter in Strasburg in 1442. But no disaster was
foreseen in 1448 when Arnold Gelthius stood surety for the
loan. The interest on the St. Thomas money had been paid
regularly, and the inventor appeared to be solvent. His
printing presses were in production, and what the existing
evidence shows that he did print is certainly only a fraction
of what he must have printed. There was an astronomical
calendar for 1448 which should have been printed in 1447,
and doubtless was; and there are fragments of several
editions of Donatus's Latin grammar—a dry-as-dust collection of conjugations and paradigms which, in manuscript,
had been inflicted on schoolboys for centuries. The calendar
and the Donatuses are printed in a version of the 36-line
Bible type.

It must have been soon after this that Gutenberg met
Johann Fust. Fust can best be described as a financier. He may
have been a goldsmith, as his brother Jacob was. Gutenberg
and Johann came to an agreement by which Fust was to
advance eight hundred gulden for equipment, on no other
security, it seems, than that of the equipment itself when it

was made. In addition, Fust agreed to pay to Gutenberg three hundred gulden each year for living expenses, wages, rent, parchment, paper, etc. The interest on the loan was to be six per cent. It is clear that the invention, and its development, was still swallowing money.

On the ground of this agreement Fust has been criticized as a sharp dealer, but he did no more than any lender to ensure that his principal was secure; in fact he did less. The agreement seems to be weighted entirely in Gutenberg's favour. Moreover, if Gutenberg's belief was correct, that he had only to pay back the eight hundred gulden to be free, notwithstanding the three hundred gulden per annum, the agreement, by any count, showed nothing but generosity on Fust's part. Unfortunately, no copy of the agreement itself has survived, and what is known of it is known only by reference and inference from a later record, the instrument written out in 1455 by the notary Ulrich Helmasperger, containing part of the proceedings of the suit of Fust against Gutenberg. It seems reasonable that there must have been some other provision for Fust's benefit, a share in the profits, perhaps.

Gutenberg maintained that Fust never fully honoured the agreement, in that the eight hundred gulden was not paid immediately and entire, but in instalments, and irregularly. If this was so, certainly its value to the inventor must have been much reduced, while the effect of wondering if he would ever receive the balance, and having to press for it, would be unhappy, and an interruption of his work. Perhaps he said as much, and more, with something of the asperity experienced by Schotten Lawel the shoemaker. Whatever the reason, a new agreement was reached, by which the annual amount of three hundred gulden was cancelled in favour of a second lump sum of eight hundred gulden. While the first eight hundred was meant for the making of tools and equipment, the second eight hundred was expressly allocated for 'the work of the books'.

Fust was to get his six per cent interest as before, but again there is no indication of anything else he might have expected, or of the security on which he made the advance.

Sixteen hundred gulden was a small fortune, and it looks as though Fust lent it out at considerable risk.

Gutenberg evidently had some equipment before he met Fust—moulds and matrices, the 36-line Bible type, and at least one press. With the new equipment from the first of Fust's loans, and working capital in addition, he ought to have produced a great deal of printing during the next four years. If he did, there is no record of it. Some authorities think that the 36-line Bible was printed during this period, though others, admitting that some parts were printed as early as 1450, will not commit themselves to anything more definite than 'before 1460'. The date 1460, however, is based on nothing stronger than a manuscript date written in one surviving copy, and the fact that some fragments of a leaf were found in the binding of a book known to have been bound in that year.

At this time Gutenberg may also have started on the printing of the 42-line Bible. It seems very extraordinary that two Bibles should have been in production at the same time, but it is equally odd that one Bible should have been begun and stopped while another one was completed, and then continued again. One hypothesis or the other is what the evidence appears to show. Whatever the facts, the inventor seems to have staked a good deal of Fust's money on the propagation of the Gospel, and no doubt he did so because he thought the Bible was sure to sell. He was, of course, entirely right, though a trifle ahead of his time.

There is some possibility that the 42-line Bible was produced in 1453, and if it was it must have been wholly Gutenberg's work; but it is more commonly supposed to have appeared in 1455, and that it was completed and published by Fust and Schoeffer, and not by Gutenberg. For in 1454 the partnership with Fust split, and Fust sued Gutenberg for the return of his capital, with interest, a total of 2,026 gulden. There is no record of the reason for the split, but presumably Fust had not gained whatever it was he had expected to gain from the arrangement, and saw no possibility of gaining it, and now he determined to have the management of the printing office in his own hands. It was

in vain for Gutenberg to argue that though interest had been
allowed for in the agreement, Fust had said privately that he
did not propose to collect it. Any court would obviously treat
such an assertion as childish and ridiculous. If a man signs a
document, he is expected to understand it and to be prepared
to implement its conditions. The truth is surely that Gutenberg had no defence, and no money anyway. The court
found against him and awarded Fust his claim, with interest, and interest on the interest, the latter, it appears,
because Fust alleged that he had had himself to borrow the
money at interest from among Christians and Jews. It was
required that Fust should swear to this borrowing, and in
1455 he came with his brother Jacob to the Convent of the
Barefooted Monks in Mainz to swear the oath before Ulrich
Helmasperger the notary. The two parties, Fust's and Gutenberg's, were to meet in the refectory between eleven and
twelve o'clock in the morning, but when Fust came there
between these hours there was no sign of Gutenberg. The
two Fusts waited, but Gutenberg did not come then, nor did
he come at all. Perhaps in disdain he would not, or in despair
could not. But at last he sent two of his servants, Heinrich
Keffer and Bechtolf von Hanau, each of whom became
notable printers afterwards in other towns. These two seem
to have lost themselves and were found by the Fusts after a
search in another part of the convent. They were upbraided
by Johann Fust, who said that he had been waiting since
before twelve, and was still waiting, for his opponent Johann
Gutenberg. The word 'opponent' is like a blow, that word
so often heir to the word 'partner'. Keffer and von Hanau
said they had been sent by their master to hear and see what
should happen. That was enough for Fust. The oath was
sworn and the judgement was thereby fastened on Gutenberg. Among the witnesses was one Peter of Gernsheim.

Gutenberg certainly could not pay the money demanded,
and Fust therefore seized his security, the tools, types, and
presses that had been made with the first loan of eight hundred gulden. Indeed, this seizure seems to have been made
already in 1454, for in that year there were two printing
houses in Mainz, and each of them was printing editions of

Incipit prefacio beati iheronimi presbi-
teri in libru actuum apliar ·

Lucas ant psalmista: ambula-
bunt de virtutibz in vir-
tutes. Post apostoli pau-
li epistolas dudum uno
uobis uol lumine translatas · domini-
on et rogatiane carissimi · actue a
postolorū compellitis ut translferam
in latinū : quē librū nulli dubiū est a
luca anthiomeno arte medico· qm postea
insecutus paulo apostolo usq̃ ad sac-
est discipul' fuisse editu . Et cuius pre-
mit imposita septi oneris magnitudo:
quia studia inuidorū reprehensione
digna putant ea que scribimus. Illo-
rum nunqz odio et detractione · iu-
uante cristo meum silebit eloquium.
Lucas igit anthiocensis · natione si-
rus· cuius laus in euangelio canit · a
pud antiochia medicine artis egregi
us · et apostolos cristi disciplus fuit :
postea usqz ad confessione paulū secu-
tus apostolū· sine crimine ? uirginita-
te pmanes·deo maluit seruire. Qui o-
ctogita z quatuor ānos erans agēs i
bithinia obiit plenus spiritu sancto :
quo instigāte i achae partibz euange
lium scribes·grecis fidelibz incarnati
onem dūi fideli narratione ostendit :
cuiusqz ex stirpe dauid descendisse mon-
strauit. Cui nō immerito scribendorū
actuū apostolicoz potestas i ministe-
rio datur:ut deo in deū pleno·et filio
pditionis extincto·oratione ab aposto
lis facta · sorte dominice electionis nu
merus compleat̄ : sicq̃ pauli cōsum-
matione apostolicus actibus daret ·
q̃diu cōtra stimulū calcitrante dūs e-
legisset. Quod legentibz et requirētibz
deū breui uolu ostendere sermone :
q̃ prolixus aliquid fastidientibus

probidisse:scies q̃ operāte agricolā
oportet de suis fructibus edere. Quem
ita diuina subsecuta ē gratia:ut non
solum corporibz sed mā animabus-
eius proficeret medicina. Explicit pre
facio. Incipit librus actuum apliar um.

Primū quidē sermo-
nem fea de omibus
o theophile q̃ cepit
iħsus facere et doce-
re:usqz i diem qua
precipies apostolis
per spiritu sāctū quos elegit assumptus
est. Quibz et prebuit seipm uiuū post
passione suā multis argumentis·p̃r
dire quadragita apparens eis · z lo-
quens de regno dei . Et uescēs prece
pit eis iherosolimis ne discederent·sed
respectarent pmissione patris quā au-
distis inquit p os meū:quia ioħānes
quidem baptizauit aqua:uos autem
baptizabimini spiritu sancto nō post
multos hos dies . Igitur q̃ conuene-
rant interrogabāt eum dicens. Dūe:
si in tepore hoc restitues regnū isrl?
Dixit aūt eis. Non ē uestrū nosse tepo-
ra uel momenta que pater posuit i sua
potestate:sed accipietis uirtutem super
uenientis spiritus sancti i uos : z eritis
michi testes in iherusalē et in omni iudea
et samaria·z usqz ad ultimū terre. Et
cum hec dixisset:uidentibus illis eleua-
tus ē·z nubes suscepit eū ab oclis eoru.
Cumqz intuerent in celū euntem illu:ecce
duo uiri astiterunt iuxta illos i uestibz
albis:qui z dixerūt. Viri galilei quid
statis aspicientes in celū? Hic iħsus q̃
assumptus est a uobis i celū:sic uenu-
et quēadmodū uidistis eum euntem i
celum. Tunc reuersi sūt iherosolimā a
monte qui uocat̄ oliueti qui ē iuxta
iherusalē:sabbati habens iter. Et cum

I. THE 42-LINE BIBLE

Incipit epistola sancti Jeronimi ad Paulinum presbiterum de omnibus diuine hystorie libris Capitulum primum.

Rater am-
brosius mi-
chi tua munuscula perferens de-
tulit simul et suauissimas litteras: que a principio amiciciaz
fidem iam probate fidei et ueteris
amicicie noua preferebant: Ue-
ra eni illa necessitudo est et xpi
glutino copulata quam non uti-
litas rei familiaris non presen-
tia tantum corporum non subdola
et palpans adulacio: sed dei timor
et diuinarum scripturarum studia con-
ciliant. legimus in ueteribus histori-
is quosdam lustrasse prouincias
nouas adisse populos maria tra-
sisse: ut eos quos ex libris no-
uerant coram qz uiderent. Sic pita-
goras memphiticos uates sic
plato egiptum et architam tareti-
num eamqz oram ytalie que quondam magna grecia dicebat la-
boriosissime peragrauit ut qui
atheis magister erat et potens cuiusqz doctrinas achademie gig-
nasia personabat fieret peregrin
atqz discipulus malens aliena
uerecude discere qua sua impu-
denter ingerere. Denique cum litteras
quasi toto orbe fugientes perseque-
tur captus a piratis et uenunda-

tus etiam tyranno crudelissimo pa-
ruit ductus captiuus uinctus
et seruus Tamen quia philosophus
maior emente se fuit. Ad tytum li-
uium lacteo eloquencie fonte ma-
nantem de ultimis hispanie gal-
liarumqz finibus quosdam uenisse
nobiles legimus et quos ad con-
templacionem sui roma non
traxerat unius hominis fama p-
duxit. Habuit illa etas inaudi-
tum omnibus seculis celebrandumqz
miraculum ut urbem tantam ingres-
si aliud extra urbem quererent.
Apollonius siue ille magus
ut uulgus loquitur siue philosophus ut pytagorici tradunt: in-
trauit psas pertransiuit caucasu
albanos scitas massagetas
opulentissima regni indie pene-
trauit et ad extremum latissimo philo-
amne transmisso peruenit ad brag-
manas ut hyarcam in throno
sedentem aureo et de tantali fonte
potantem inter paucos discipu-
los de natura de moribz de die-
rum ac syderum cursu audiret doce-
tem. Inde per elamitas babiloni-
os chaldeos medos assirios
parthos syros phenices ara-
bes palestinos reuersus alexan-
driam perrexit ethiopiam ut gym-
nosophistas et famosissimam
solis mensam uideret in sabulo:
Inuenit ille uir ubiqz quod disce-
ret et semper proficiens semper se me-

the same indulgence for Paul Zappe, the chief commissioner for the sale of these indulgences in Germany. There was reason for haste. The previous commissioner had defrauded the papal authorities, and was in prison, and in consequence Zappe was left with the problem of producing a new supply of indulgences in a diminished time. An indulgence was nothing but a document, issued on papal authority, which promised forgiveness of a man's sins in return for his contribution to this or that charity or cause; in this instance the money was intended for the defence of Cyprus. The contributor's name and the date were entered on the paper or vellum, when the sale was made, by the pardoner who acted as the channel of distribution for these things. The indulgence we are now concerned with evidently sold like hot cakes, for Zappe employed two printers to print it, one alone not producing enough, and each of these printers reprinted it several times. It is abundantly clear that if printing had not been invented, there must have been rather more elbow room in the halls of heaven.

The two indulgences printed by the rival printers are so similar in layout that it looks as though one of the printers set it first, and that printer not being able to keep up to the demand, the other printer was asked to copy it. If Gutenberg still had the materials he had possessed before his agreement with Fust, the 36-line Bible type in particular, then we know which indulgence is his, and I believe that it was the first, and so the other printer's work was the copy. It is a much more printerly and scholarly piece of work than the other, which seems to show uncertainty of technique and insufficiency of material. Such defects are to be expected in a newly founded workshop.

No doubt the rival printers were Johann Fust and his partner Peter Schoeffer, that Peter of Gernsheim who was the witness of Gutenberg's ruin in the convent of the Barefooted Monks. Where did this man come from, and what was he that should suddenly become a printer? Fust was not a printer, and probably knew very little of the technique of the work. If he were to start a printing business of his own, he would have need of a man who knew how to deal

4. The two indulgences printed for Paul Zappe by two rival
printers in Mainz in 1454. Appropriate spaces for names and dates

Vniuersis Christi fidelibus presentes litteras inspecturis **Paulinus** Chappe Consiliarius ambassiator et procurator generalis Serenissimi Regis Cypri pro pace predicta in domino Ihesu Christo salutem … affectum …

Forma plenissime absolutionis et remissionis in vita

Misereatur tui … Dominus noster Ihesus Christus per sua sanctissima et piissima misericordia te absoluat Et auctoritate beatorum petri et pauli apostolorum eius ac dicte apostolica mihi commissa et tibi concessa Ego te absoluo ab omnibus peccatis tuis … In nomine patris et filii et spiritus sancti amen.

Forma plenarie remissionis in mortis articulo

Misereatur tui … Dominus noster … per sua sanctissima … Ego te absoluo ab omnibus peccatis tuis contritis confessis et oblitis restituendo te vnitati … et sacramentis ecclesie Remittendo tibi penas purgatorii quas propter culpas et offensas incurristi dando tibi plenissimam … In nomine patris et filii et spiritus sancti amen.

Uniuersis Cristi fidelibus presentes litteras inspecturis ₽ audituris Salutem in domino Cum dominus noster Nicolaus diuina prouidentia papa quintus ... Regno Cypri in hac parte Saluti dño Cū ... diue memorie Thomae et Sauernos gratio ... omnibus xpi fidelibus ... ... Institutore ... ₽ apostonice singule dñi nostri ihu xpi pie exhortatio qui infra triennui a primadie ... anni domini Quattuorcenti inpictonis ₽ ... ... lice fides ₽ regnū pдti de facultatibz suis magne uel minne, put ipos videbitur ... ... subuentione pie erogauerint ... tint ut ... ... podne ... singulares ... regulares ... ₽ ipos digendi confessiones eoz audiris, ₽ cōmissis etiam ... inpnie reseruatis excepti criminibz atq; defectis quatiescūq; grauibz ₽ una vice tantū debita absolutione impedire ₽ penitentia Saluratem inuigere Menē ... huiuser petierit ipos a quibuscūqz excomunicationis suspensionū ₽ interdicti aliisq; sententiis ... ecclesiastice a iure uel ab hoie ...mulgatio quibz forsan innodati existūt absoluere. Iniūcta ₽ modo culpe penitentia Salutari uel aliae ₽ de iure fuerint iniugeda ... eos de quibz ore cōfessi ₽ corde cōtriti fuerint Indulgentia ac plenaria remissionē efficeri nō poterit Signa atrocioni officiendo plenissimū oīm peccatz suoz ₽ cedere valeat. Satisfactione ₽ eos factas, Si supuixerint aut ₽ eoz heredibz si tūc transierint ... ... a unū ānuū Singulis Sextis ferijs uel quodā alia die ieiunet. legitimo inpedimento ecclesie precepto regulari obseruātia pnia iniūcta ... ... uoto uel alias nō obstū. Et ipo inpeditio in dicto ānno uel siue parte, anno sequēti uel aliae quam primū poterint iciugabit ... ... in aliquo annor. uel eoz parte dicta ieiuniū ... adimplere nequiuerit Confessor oid electus ... ... alioqui dicta ... illa ... ... opa qi ipi facere etiam renebit. O modo oī ex ₽ fidentia remissionis huioi quod absit peccandi pnumat ... Aliqui ... sint roborio uel momentā Et quia deuoti ... ... de facultatibus suis pie erogaueir merito huiusmodi indulgentijs gaudere debet. In veritatis testimoniu sigilla ... ... pntibz litis testimonialibus est appensum Datum in opp ... ... anno dñi Quadragito die vero ... ... mense ...

Forma plenissime absolutionis et remissionis in vita

Misereatur tui &c Dominus noster ihesus xpristus per sua sanctissima et piissima mia; et absoluat Et aute ipso ... ... petri ₽ pauli apostolr̄ eius ac auctoritate apostolica michi cōmissa tibi cōcessa Ego te absoluo ab omnibz peccatis tuis cōtritis cōfessis ₽ oblitis Etiam ab omnibz casibz excessibz criminibz atqz delictis quātūcūq; grauibz sedi aplice reseruatis Nec nō a quibuslibz excoiationū suspensionū ₽ interdicti Aliisqz sentencijs censuris ₽ penis ecclesiasticis a iure uel ab hoie ₽mulgatis Siquas incurristi dando tibi plenissimā oīm peccōn̄ tuor̄ indulgentiā ₽ remissionē Inquantū claues sancte matris ecclesie in hac parte se extendūt. In noīe patris ₽ filij ₽ spiritus sancti Amen

Forma plenarie remissionis in mortis articulo

Misereatur tui &c Dominus noster ut supra Ego te absoluo ab omnibz peccatis tuis cōtritis cōfessis et oblitis restituendo te vnitati fideliū ₽ sacramentoz, ecclesie Remittendo tibi penas purgatorij quas propter culpas ₽ offensas incurristi dando tibi plenariā oīm peccōn̄ tuor̄ remissionē Inquantū claues sancte matris ecclesie in hac parte se extendūt. In noīe patris ₽ filij ₽ spiritus sancti Amen with type and presses. This Peter of Gernsheim could have learned his business nowhere but in Gutenberg's house as one of Gutenberg's workmen. Was he placed there by a far-seeing Fust? Whether or no, Fust undoubtedly had an eye for a likely man, and the man himself knew very well on which side his bread was buttered. The power and the money were with Fust, and so Peter went with him, and clinched it by marrying his daughter. He became a capable printer, indeed, the best of his time, and if he completed the 42-line Bible, planned by Gutenberg, he did it competently—more, gloriously.

The new firm had capital, and it had youth and enthusiasm, and it forged ahead, out of obscurity and into the light of definitive history. Gutenberg was old, utterly frustrated, and burdened with debt. Although the city of Mainz paid annuities to him in 1455, he seems to have had no real income, and he may have had to sell his printing equipment to live. It is certain that the 36-line Bible types, very much worn, were in the hands of Albrecht Pfister, a printer of Bamberg, in 1461, though how he got them is a matter for conjecture. Gutenberg's finances went from bad to worse, and in 1458 St. Thomas's Chapter, which had received its interest regularly all these years on the loan made in 1442, had to make threats for the return of its money. It did not get it, however, despite repeated applications for the arrest of Gutenberg, and eventually it had to write off the loan.

Gutenberg disappeared into obscurity. Some work has been credited to him during this period, notably the 36-line Bible itself, though how he could have printed that great book at such a nadir of his fortunes, it is difficult to understand. He is also credited, hesitantly, with the printing of a book called the *Catholican,* another large work, but where he printed it, if he did, is equally unknown. It is assumed by some writers that he went to Eltville, a village near Mainz, where his family had estates, and if so, he escaped harm in the sack of Mainz, which put Fust and Schoeffer's office out of action for a time. This commotion was the result of the strife between the two rival archbishops which was at last brought to a decision by force of arms. Diether, in possession of the see, was a gentle man, and well liked in Mainz. Adolf, his opponent, was a man of action, ruthless and decisive, and he had collected an army outside the city walls. He invaded the city, sacked it, and displaced Diether, and then made his headquarters at Eltville.

Once in power, Adolf does not seem to have been an unkindly man, nor an unperceptive one, and in 1465 he took pity on the ageing inventor and appointed him a noble of his court. There he was maintained in peace and comfort.

Nevertheless, he was still printing. Whether he had any equipment of his own is not known, but he did have equipment, lent to him by Dr. Konrad Humery. This was still in his possession when he died, which suggests that he had been using it until the last, though what he may have printed with it has not been discovered. Printed matter has often proved most ephemeral when we would have wished it most enduring. In more than twenty years of printing Gutenberg must have been responsible for a large amount of printed work but it has almost all vanished, and much of what remains is often ascribed by some authorities to someone else. Gutenberg never set his name or his mark on anything he did, and the result has been endless controversy and disagreement among the scholars of all nations. But he did not live for the sake of scholars of a following age. He was a man with a ruling passion, and once he had found the channel that gave him at least the reward of achievement, he stayed in it, working out a principle of printing that remains virtually unchanged until the present day, and a method that was to survive unaltered into the nineteenth century.

He died in 1467 or 1468. Even the date of his death is uncertain, like everything else about him, but it may be deduced from the application made by Dr. Humery to the archbishop for the return of the property he had lent to Gutenberg. It was returned, but only on the condition that it should not be sold outside the city. Gutenberg was probably buried in the Franciscan church at Mainz. This church was demolished in the eighteenth century, and there is now no trace of his tomb.

So the man who made possible the dissemination of all

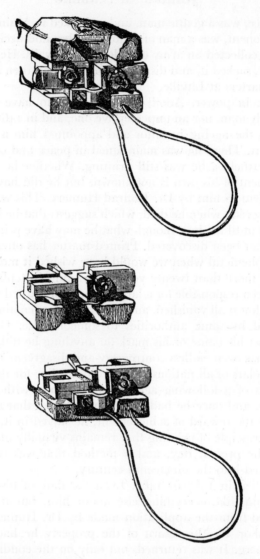

5. An eighteenth-century type mould. Outwardly unlike the object shown in Jost Amman's engraving, and no doubt equally unlike anything Gutenberg used, its principles and theirs must be fundamentally the same. In this example the long 'rat's tail' is a wire spring that holds the matrix in place. The second illustration shows the mould opened as it was every time a letter was cast.

knowledge over all the world and to all posterity, himself left
little trace of his person and story, and died in the end
broken and obscure. This and every book is his monument.

We can only conjecture what Gutenberg really did invent.
If we accept him as the inventor of printing, he must, as I
have said already, have invented the mould for casting type.
The invention of printing by movable types was essentially
the invention of a satisfactory method of making those types,

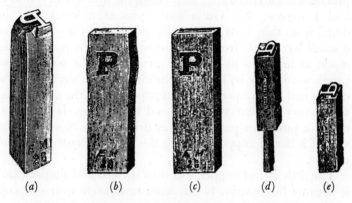

(a)   (b)   (c)   (d)   (e)

6. The process of the manufacture of type at any period is illustrated by these nineteenth-century wood-engravings. First, the
letter is cut in relief on the end of a bar of metal; after hardening,
this bar, now a punch, is struck into softer metal to produce a
'strike'; dressed and squared, the strike becomes a matrix, which
in conjunction with a mould is used to cast letters; the tang or
tail of surplus metal is broken off the newly cast type, which is
then dressed to make it ready for the compositor.

of a technique of setting them one with another to form
pages, and then of printing from them.

In the casting of type a mould is necessary to cast the
shank or body of the letter, and it must be adjustable so that
it will cast all widths of body, from the narrowest, like that
of the i to that of, say, a capital M, and each body or shank
must be truly rectangular. The mould must be made of a
metal that will endure the heat of casting, and which is
yet easy to work. Modern moulds are made of steel, but

Gutenberg's mould may have been made of copper or some such softer metal.

The mould casts the body of the type, and it is used in conjunction with another mould, called the matrix, which casts the face or letter of the type. There must be a matrix for each different letter. The technique involved in the making of a matrix is not at all simple or easy, but some method must have been worked out early in the fifteenth century, for a mould is no use without matrices. The whole process was carried out by hand until the nineteenth century, and I suggest that Gutenberg's process differed only in detail from this. First the letter is cut in relief on the end of a small bar of soft iron, with files and scrapers, proofs being made at intervals to show the progress of the work; these proofs were made by smoking the character in the flame of a candle and then impressing it on paper. When the cutting was satisfactory the bar was hardened by heating. It was then called a punch or patrix. It was driven by a blow into the side of a bar of copper, leaving the letter indented into the copper.

The little bar of copper was then dressed and shaped, and it became the matrix. It was fixed in position over one end of the aperture of the mould, and molten lead was poured into the other end. The mould was then opened to release a small bar of lead or type metal, bearing the character on one end. Many others exactly like it could be made in sequence.

The cutting of a punch, the making of a matrix, and the casting of type are each distinct skills needing training and experience for success. Yet these things must have been done by the inventor of printing. He may have conceived the method and made the equipment stage by stage, and at each stage he must have had the perception, sooner or later, to see that repeated failure was not necessarily due to the tools, but to the lack of experience of the hand that used them.

His type made at last, he would next have to work out a method of composing it. Anything that prints directly on to paper must have the letters in reverse if they are to show the right way round. The familiar rubber stamp is a convenient

example of this. The separate letters of the type must therefore be assembled in an order the reverse of that in which
they appear on the paper, and the modern compositor does
this in the only way in which it can conveniently be done by
hand. Any other way must be wearisome, unsatisfactory, and
much more productive of errors. Gutenberg must have found
this way of doing it, if not in every convenience of detail, then

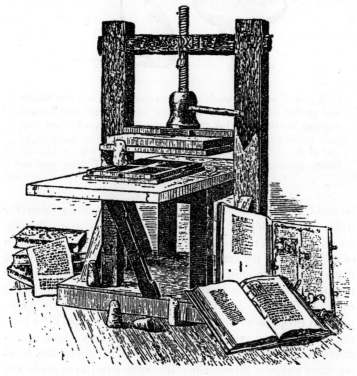

7. This imaginary representation of Gutenberg's press may be
near the truth. The forme of type rests on a flat bed or table, on
which it would be inked and have the paper laid on it; the forme
would then be pushed under the platen and the impression
achieved by turning the screw with the wooden bar.

in the main principle. When the page of type is at last set
and ready for printing, it must, as it is a collection of loose
and separate letters, in some way be held together so that it

may be carried to the press without danger of falling asunder. It could be held in a tray, as modern type is held in a galley on a proof press, but if it were it would still have to be held tight by some means, for letters that are not tightly pressed one against the other will not print properly. It could also

8. A pair of ink balls made of leather joined to a wooden handle and stuffed with hair or wool. They were rubbed and banged together to distribute ink that was put on them, and then they were applied to the forme. Extant examples of printing, up to the end of the eighteenth century, show them to have been, in most hands, singularly incompetent implements, but there was no alternative until the roller arrived.

be held in a frame, and if it were, the arrangement for tightening the letters together must be even more certain, for otherwise they would inevitably drop through the bottom of the frame. If the tray or frame has four sides, the obvious thing to do is to squeeze the type into one corner of it by means of wedges or screws pressing against two adjacent sides. If the type has been accurately cast and the composition properly done, such pressure will convert even type in an open frame into a firm and portable unit which nowadays we call a forme, and which indeed Gutenberg may himself have called a forme, since this very word appears in the documents.

The press itself was not something that Gutenberg had to invent, but rather something that he need only adapt. There were several kinds of press in existence that could be used to produce an impression from a forme of type, but none that could be considered convenient for the production of repeated impressions. What was wanted was some simple means of withdrawing the forme from the press so that it might be inked, the paper be laid upon it, and the whole be returned under the press for the next impression. Later printers did this by having the type on a movable bed, which could be slid under the press and out again with ease. Without this device or something at least equally expeditious, the printing of any book must be utterly wearisome, and perhaps so prodigal of time that the advantages of printing—which is convenience of duplication—would be seriously reduced. I think it must be assumed that Gutenberg had some such device—if it were only an extension of the bed.

The problems of an inventor are seldom simple. Too often the solution of one problem only clears the way to another. There can be few inventors in all history whose problems were as numerous and diverse as those of the inventor of printing, and to say, as some do, that printing was invented in 1454, or in 1455, is childish and silly. The invention must have been a matter of dogged perseverance through many years and many failures, through poverty and disaster, and it is only comparatively recently that we have come to perceive, besides the sociological significance of the invention of printing, the remarkable technical achievement of its inventor.

WILLIAM CAXTON

THE INTRODUCTION OF
PRINTING INTO ENGLAND

'WHEN I remember that every man is bounden by the commandment and counsel of the wise man to eschew sloth and idleness, which is mother and nourisher of vices, and ought to put myself into virtuous occupation and business, then I, having no great charge of occupation, . . . took a French book and read therein many strange and marvellous histories. . . . And for so much as this book was new and late made and drawn into the French, and never had seen it in our English tongue, I thought in myself it should be a good business to translate it into our English, to the end that it might be had as well in the royaume of England as in other lands. And forthwith took pen and ink, and began to run forth as blind Bayard in this present work, which is named "The Recuyell of the Trojan Histories". And afterwards when I remembered myself of my simpleness and unperfectness that I had in both languages, that is to wit in French and in English, for in France was I never, and was born and learned my English in Kent, in the Weald, where I doubt not is spoken as broad and rude English as any place in England, and have continued for the space of thirty years for the most part in Brabant, Flanders, Holland, and Zealand. And thus when all these things came before me, after that I had made and written five or six quires, I fell in despair of this work, and purposed no more to have continued therein, and those quires laid apart, and in two years after laboured no more

28

in this work, and was fully in will to have left it, till on a time it fortuned that . . . my lady Margaret . . . my sovereign lord, Duchess of Burgundy . . . sent for me to speak with her good grace about divers matters, among which I let her Highness have knowledge of this work, which anon commanded me to show the said five or six quires to her said Grace; and when she had seen them, anon she found a default in my English, which she commanded me to amend and moreover commanded me straitly to continue and make an end of the residue then not translated; whose dreadful commandment I durst in no wise disobey, because I am a servant unto her said Grace and receive of her yearly fee and other many good and great benefits (and also hope many more to receive of her Highness), but forthwith went and laboured in the said translation after my simple and poor cunning. . . .'

'Thus endeth the second book of the Recule of the Histories of Troy. Which books were late translated into French out of Latin by the labour of the venerable person Raoul le Feure, priest, as afore is said; and by me indigne and unworthy, translated into this rude English by commandment of my said redoubted Lady, Duchess of Burgundy. And forasmuch as I suppose the said two books be not had before this time in our English language, therefore I had the better will to accomplish this said work; which was begun in Bruges, and continued in Ghent and finished in Cologne, in the time of the troublous world, and of the great divisions being and reigning, as well in the royaumes of England and France as in all other places universally throughout the world; that is to wit the year of our Lord a thousand four hundred seventy one. . . .'

'Thus end I this book, which I have translated after mine Author as nigh as God hath given me cunning, to whom be given the laud and praising. And forasmuch as in the writing of the same my pen is worn, my hand weary and not steadfast, mine eyne dimmed with overmuch looking on the white paper, and my courage not so prone and ready to labour as it hath been, and that age creepeth on me daily

29

and feebleth all the body, and also because I have promised
to divers gentlemen and my friends to address to them as
hastily as I might this said book, therefore I have practised
and learned at my great charge and dispence to ordain this
said book in print, after the manner and form as ye may here
see, and is not written with pen and ink as other books be,
to the end that every man might have them at once. For all
the books of this story . . . were begun in one day and also
finished in one day, which book I have presented to my said
redoubted Lady. . . .'

In these quotations from the prologue of one and the
epilogues of two of the three books of the English version of
The Recuyell of the Histories of Troye, the character of William
Caxton shines out. In the antique words and turns of phrase
a man is shown who might sit comfortably by the fire to talk
of the chivalry and the knightly adventure that were vanish-
ing from the world; of the disappearance of jousts, which
were rare nowadays and ought to be revived to enliven the
courage of men; and of deeds of daring and heroism by
noble champions to light a darkling world. Caxton loved a
gallant story, but he was not because of that an idle man.
On the contrary, the conventional phrases about the avoid-
ance of sloth were spoken by him in all sincerity. He would
not allow the hours to pass emptily away, and it was because
he gave himself occupation by setting about a translation
from the French that he was led to learn the new craft of
printing, and so became the first printer in England and a
notability in the literature of his native country.

At the age of fifty years or thereabouts Caxton came upon
a new life. He had come to the Low Countries as a youth,
probably in the train of a master to whom he was apprenticed, and there he had remained 'for the space of thirty
years', prospering and earning the respect of his fellows in
the English colony, so much so that they appointed him
eventually to lead and govern the organization created by
the Mercers and the Merchant Adventurers and called the
English Nation. To be Governor of the English Nation in the
Low Countries was certainly to be an important man. It

involved business with all sorts of eminent people, and it meant negotiations at the highest level when the King of England and the Duke of Burgundy quarrelled and banned all trading between their territories, and it brought to Caxton the friendship of a princess of England, his 'redoubted' Duchess of Burgundy.

Caxton was certainly a lover of books—a great reader of books in Latin, French, and English, and perhaps in other languages, in Flemish surely, and in German perhaps; but there is no evidence that he ever set his own hand to the writing or the making of a book until he conceived the notion of putting the *Recuyell* into English. His initial enthusiasm for that task suffered the diminution common among authors, who grow dissatisfied with their work and abandon what is really a perfectly good beginning for lack of confidence in themselves; and perhaps take up the remnant years afterwards and complete it. So Caxton did. He needed only a little push, only a command for him to lean upon, and he was fairly off on his new career, when men begin to think of retiring, which was to lead him at last to the Almonry at Westminster and into the history book.

The *Recuyell* was a success. The Lady Margaret received it with pleasure, and then others began to ask for copies, various friends and perhaps high-placed persons who could not easily be refused. There was nothing for it but to write the whole book out again for each copy that was needed, and Caxton apparently did this himself. To copy by hand all the contents of a very long work is labour enough; to have to do it several times over is a penance; and to have to do it for a book you have yourself written is a torture, as any author will sympathetically understand. It is no wonder that Caxton should complain that his hand was weary and not steadfast, his eyne dimmed with overmuch looking on the white paper; no wonder that he sought for some means of lightening his labour.

He had been in Cologne, and in that city there was a man called Ulrich Zell, who made books by that curious method that had been contrived in Mainz twenty years and more ago by Johann Gutenberg; that method by which books were not made as a scribe would make them, one at a time and starting at the beginning and following through to the end, but by starting a hundred, or two hundred, or even more, all at once on one day, and proceeding so, wholesale, finish them all off on another day. Whatever the secret of this mystery, it was exactly what Caxton wanted, and he therefore had his book printed for him, at his great expense. More than that, according to Winkyn de Worde, who was Caxton's foreman in England later, and should know, Caxton learned the business of printing in Cologne, and perhaps it was in the printing of his own book that he served his late apprenticeship to printing.

It used to be thought that Caxton learned his printing in Bruges, and that it was a printer called Colard Mansion who taught him. William Blades, Caxton's nineteenth-century biographer, thought so, in defiance of Winkyn de Worde; but that view is no longer accepted. Rather, the reverse seems to be the fact, that Caxton brought the knowledge from Cologne, and taught Mansion, who had been a calligrapher.

Together, it appears, they set up business as printers in Bruges. Their press they would have made for them after the pattern of the one Caxton had seen in Cologne, or they might find, in Cologne or elsewhere, a man who had already constructed a press and therefore would know how to construct another. The type was a different matter. Punches and moulds and matrices cannot be made by anyone, nor is type easily cast. They would look about for some ready source of supply, and it is likely that they bought type from Jan Veldener of Louvain, who was using at this time a type very like the one that Caxton and Mansion used in some of their early books.

But their first book, *The Recuyell of the Histories of Troye*, was in a different type, a kind of letter called bâtarde, which was possibly made by them and modelled on Mansion's calligraphic hand. It is a bold, irregular letter, but readable.

When printers in other towns had already learned various little tricks of their trade which made work easier and more efficient, the two printers in Bruges struggled along with antique techniques that are clearly visible in their books. Indeed, Caxton learned his trade very slowly, and year after

32

III. CAXTON PRESENTING A COPY OF THE RECUYELL TO MARGARET,
DUCHESS OF BURGUNDY

IV. WILLIAM CASLON

year was content with methods that a little ingenuity, or some correspondence with another printer, would quickly have shown to be obsolete. All the Bruges books, for example, have lines of uneven length on the right-hand side, like a written letter, and so too have those printed by Caxton long after in England; and this was simply because he and Mansion did not know, or if they did know would not use, that most simple of typographical conveniences, a setting rule. Type is set line by line in a composing stick. After the first line is set, the second may be started, setting the type immediately on top of the first line. Now a line of sixty or seventy characters will not lie so flat that it will present a smooth surface; some of the letters are bound to project, however slightly, beyond their fellows, and this makes it difficult to move the next line about, the edge of one type catching on the edge of another. If any line is to be spaced out to the full measure, as type always is today, it must be moved about, to exchange the spaces between the words. Now if you try to slide type about that has other type below it, sooner or later, as any compositor will tell you, the inevitable will happen and the line will fall into pie. The difficulty can be avoided, as the early printers avoided it, and as Caxton avoided it, by not spacing the words out, so that the ends of the line fall unevenly on the printed page. It can also be avoided simply by laying a strip of smooth metal over the line already set in the stick and setting the next line on that, when the type can be moved just as desired, and no impediment interferes with the spacing out of the line.

Caxton apparently did not know of this device, and felt no impulse to think of it for himself, though it was in use by this time by printers in many other towns around Bruges. He was not, however, a mechanically inventive man, and he was not a technician. He was never even a good printer, in the sense that Fust and Schoeffer were good printers. There is a good deal crude and naïve about every one of Caxton's books, something a little home-made and cumbersome. Printing meant to him something other than a mode of design; he thought of it simply as a means of dissemination, of the multiplication of books.

The *Recuyell* was printed probably in the year 1474. For two years Caxton and Mansion worked together in Bruges, printing several books, no doubt, among which was *The Game and Play of Chess Moralized*, a book in which the losses and victories and the problems of life are compared to the situations in a game of chess. This was originally written in Latin, but it had been translated into French by two separate translators, and Caxton read both of them, and used both of them in his translation into English. The introduction of one of these translations Caxton took over bodily, but so interpolated it, and so extended it, with his own comments and ideas, that it has become more Caxton's work than the original author's. A modern writer would have you in court these days for such making free with his work, but in the fifteenth century literary property was not so strictly recognized. We should be grateful for that, for otherwise we should hear Caxton's homely voice far less often than we do.

The Game and Play of Chess is printed in the same type as the *Recuyell*. Caxton later acquired a second fount of type, which he used in *Les Quatres Dernières Choses*. The type is another bâtarde, but more angular and more condensed, an unlovely letter. The book is printed in black with certain lines in red. There is clear evidence that the red and the black were printed at one and the same impression, a method that would save the bother of accurate registration and also, of course, the labour of sending the sheets through the press a second time; but like many other time-savers, it had disadvantages. The method was simple enough. The lines to be printed in red were isolated in the forme by having a line of space above and below them. The forme was inked with black all over in the usual way, and then the black was wiped off the isolated lines, which were then inked in red, probably with a finger or the ball of the thumb, after which the paper could be laid on and the two colours printed at one go of the press. If you will print by this method, you must be satisfied with a red that is a lot less brilliant than it should be, for black is always an insidious hue, and no amount of wiping in such circumstances will prevent it from sullying the red. Further, if the utmost care and accuracy in

9. One of the better examples of illustrations from Caxton's books.
It has a naïve charm. The device of showing the chessboard as
from above is evidently as deliberate as it is effective.

inking is not exercised, the red will get beyond the places it
is intended to go, and appear as red rims or tips on adjacent
letters. This is exactly what has happened in *Les Quatres
Dernières Choses*.

It might be expected that Caxton would not have minded
this as much as Mansion, for Caxton was not interested in the
fine details of appearance, while Mansion, who was a well-
known calligrapher, ought to have taken the opposite view.
In fact, the idea may have been Mansion's, for he continued
with this method long after Caxton had left him and returned
to England.

After thirty-five years on the Continent, Caxton decided
to return to his native country. He decided also to take with

him material to start a press in London, to bring to his countrymen the advantages of this revolutionary method of making books. Some writers seem to think that Caxton proposed to do this simply out of an altruistic motive to serve his country, and that his various translations of foreign works into English were items of this same altruism; as though to do such things in the nature of trade and for the making of money were somehow a shame and a taint. It is villainous nonsense. Caxton may have had enough money to live in retirement, but it is much more likely that he had not, for all the dignity of his service to the English Nation. It seems clear that he needed some means to live by when he came to England, and here was the means to hand, novel and effective and congenial.

So on a day in 1476 a train of carts must have set off from the house where Caxton and Mansion printed in Bruges, towards the port of Sluys. They would certainly be heavily laden, for in one of them there would be the founts of type that Caxton intended to use in England, carefully packed, with matrices, and perhaps also punches; in another cart, perhaps many reams of paper, for paper was not yet made in England, and Caxton, in need of quantities far larger than the scribes required, must import it, either now or later; and in another cart, the dismantled but still ponderous elements of the press, with its great screw protected by heavy wrappings.

Except for the date, all this is imagination; and yet something of the sort must have happened, for it is scarcely credible that Caxton should have started from scratch in England.

Colard Mansion remained as a printer in Bruges, but he did not prosper after Caxton left. He printed many books, but perhaps he did not have the business experience, as he certainly did not have the publishing sense, of his former partner, for he lost money. In 1480 he was so poor that he could not undertake a commission for the writing of a manuscript without advances of money to keep him going while the work was in train. His last effort in the making of books was a swan song, a beautifully illustrated edition of Ovid's

Metamorphoses. The cost of it was his final ruin, for as soon as it was finished Mansion left Bruges for ever, leaving unpaid the rent of the room over the porch of the church of St. Donatus in which he had printed his books.

Caxton's experience in London was very different. A capable man, enjoying the benevolence of people in high places, he set forth upon a tripartite career which was remarkable in all three branches. The name of Caxton as a translator is safe in English literature; as a publisher he was able to build a business any publisher would be proud to own, with a list of both popular and learned books; and as a printer, he served the two other facets of his activity conscientiously and faithfully.

His venture into publishing and printing in England was not without risk. He had no means of calculating in advance how many copies of his books he might sell, and to print too many would be as disastrous as printing too few. His market was severely limited, because literacy in fifteenth-century England was not a thing to be taken for granted. Far from it. The common people were illiterate almost entirely. Of the nobility, only some could read, and fewer would. The ladies of the great houses would find romances welcome, but even there a scholar would have to read aloud for them. It was mainly among the clergy that Caxton would find his market, for they taught the schools, and were themselves students; they were authors and translators and scribes; and they were collectors of books, the bishops and the archbishops on a grand scale, the priests and the monks on a scale more modest. Chaucer's clerk, it may be remembered, had a library—a half-dozen of books at his bed's head—and this was a considerable investment in a time when any book was a manuscript, and the most plain and utilitarian must still be expensive. In 1476, when Caxton arrived, the situation must have been much the same. Thirty years after the invention of printing, printed books must still have been rare in England, though by no means unknown.

Into this virgin field came Caxton's little caravan, bearing a burden so potent for the future, and so full of threat, that the nobles of England would certainly have sent it all

10. A reader of the kind for whom Caxton catered. Books in his
time were mostly large and frequently ponderous, and some sort
of support for them was necessary. The chest in this woodcut is the
equivalent of a modern bookshelf.

back again, or burned it all, and Caxton along with it, if
they could have perceived how their power and privileges
would in the end be destroyed by this insidious invader.

Caxton sought at once for a place to set up his press and
found it in the Almonry of Westminster Abbey, in a shop for
which he had to pay an annual rent of ten shillings. The idea
that Caxton printed his books in a side chapel of the Abbey
itself is prevalent, but it is naïve. The Almonry, originally a
place for the distribution of alms, was probably an area on

the south side of the abbey, including several shops, from the rent of which perhaps some part of the alms was derived. Caxton's shop may have been somewhere in the direction of the beginning of Tothill Street. The shop bore a shield with a vertical strip of red—a red pale, in heraldry—and it was here, at the sign of the Red Pale, that Caxton printed throughout his life, and Winkyn de Worde after him.

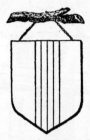

11. The sign of the Red Pale.

At that time Westminster was well outside London, and it is not clear why Caxton chose a place away from the city. Was it so that he might be near the court? Several times he claimed in his books that he worked 'under the shadow of the king's protection'. What could Caxton have done to deserve so august a patronage? It has been suggested that when Edward IV was driven out of his kingdom by the Earl of Warwick and took refuge with his brother in Bruges, Caxton was able to be of service to a king whose realm was then only a rag-tag and bobbletail of impecunious peers. If that were so, then perhaps Caxton came to Westminster to set up his press, not at a venture, but on the direct invitation of a king who had now regained his throne.

Caxton's first practical problem was the erection of his press and the general sorting out and fettling of his equipment, and the manufacture of anything that might be needed in the beginning of his new venture. None of this would give serious trouble. A much more difficult problem must have been the supply of men to staff his new printing house, for where were they to come from? There could be no printers looking for employment in England in 1476, and any men that Caxton required must therefore be brought from the Continent or be selected and trained at home. It is probable that Caxton followed both of these courses, by bringing

12. A wood-engraving showing the house in Westminster reputed to have been Caxton's.

experienced men with him to train a native staff. One of these men may have been Winkyn de Worde, from Alsace, who later became Caxton's foreman, and eventually his heir; if this is so, then de Worde at that time must have been a young man, for he lived until 1535.

It was not until November 1477 that the first book appeared from the first of English printing houses. It was *The Dictes and Sayings of the Philosophers*, 'enprynted by me William Caxton at Westmestre'. It is not a large book, since it contains only 152 pages, but it has in it one of Caxton's most delightful introductions. The book was translated by Earl Rivers, who had found himself enchanted by the French original when he read it during a pilgrimage to St. James of Compostella, and he translated it when on his return he was appointed one of the governors of the Prince of Wales. Rivers was a friend of Caxton to the end of his life, and showed invariable kindness to the printer. He also respected his ability, to the extent of asking him to oversee the translation.

Caxton read through it and carefully compared it with the original. He found that a section 'touching women', which was in the original of Socrates, had been omitted, perhaps, Caxton hazarded, because Earl Rivers was in love with some noble lady and would not offend her by publishing these criticisms of women. But then, says Caxton, they know that such faults and defects are not found in women in these parts of the world, though no doubt perceptible in the women of Greece, where people are different. But then again, perhaps no such thought was in his lordship's mind at all; perhaps it was simply that as he translated from the French manuscript, peradventure the wind had blown over the leaf. So Caxton proceeds, gently leg-pulling in a manner he could surely not have dared had he not been on good terms with his victim.

A book which attracted Caxton from the beginning was Chaucer's *Canterbury Tales*, and he must have started work on it very soon after he came to England, for he was able to put it on the market in 1478. It contained 750 pages, a large work, but not remarkable against the achievements of Continental printers of the time: the readiness with which the early printers, despite their cumbrous methods, undertook books of a thousand pages and more is astonishing. One might well imagine that they would be engaged for years on one such work, but in fact they seem to have produced them

Or elles yf he was amerous on somme noble lady + for whos loue he wolde not sette it in in his book + or elles for the vngraunce he bare vnto alle in affeccyon, loue and good wylle that he hath vnto alle ladyes and Gentilwommen, he thought that Socrates spared the sayd And Book of Wommen more than trouth Wherfore I can not thinke that so noble a Phylosophre as Socrates was sholde wryte othe

T Hus endeth the seconde book of the venue of the lyf, corde of Troye/Whiche bookes were translated By me Indigne and unworthy translatour at the comandement of my sayd good/gracyous table persone maad of ferre aforce a fort is saide/And

13. Some of the types used by Caxton. The first, with its clumsy hand-lettered initial, is from the *Recuyell of the Histories of Troye*, printed in Bruges in 1476. The second is from the *Dictes and Sayings of the Philosophers*, printed in Westminster in 1477. The third is from *Charles the Great*, printed in 1485, and the fourth from *The Royal Book*, 1487.

almost as quickly as a modern printer would produce them today.

Caxton took care to get what he believed to be an accurate manuscript of the *Canterbury Tales*, and was appalled to find, after the book was printed and finished, that his copy had not been a good one after all. When he issued a second edition of the book six years later, he had found a more reliable copy, and he expresses his gladness for this in the foreword.

Caxton was certainly a scholar, who cared for accuracy more than many did in an age when precision was not held so high in regard as it is today; and yet his books are full of typographical errors—so much so that William Blades thought that the proof-reading was scamped.

As a printer Caxton was remarkable only for his being the first in England, and for the industry he showed throughout his career. A large part of his work was done in English, which is also interesting against the constant reissue of books in Latin elsewhere. But he was always old-fashioned in his business of printing, always behindhand in technical achievement, as though he preferred to be so. For example, he did not begin to space lines out to a common measure—to justify them—until 1480, when other printers had been doing it for years. He did not achieve an illustrated book until 1481, and even then it was only with the crudest and most unsatisfactory of wood-cuts. He never did find an artist who could do good work, and he does not really seem to have cared about illustration anyway. But none of this is to deny that he was a remarkable man. If Caxton had never brought printing to England, it would undoubtedly have come within a few years—it came, indeed, in his own lifetime, and he had competitors in the city of London; but it would very likely not have come with an Englishman, and certainly he would not have embarked on printing and publishing in the vernacular, as Caxton did. We would have had instead, as we have got from the rival press, a series of dull books in Latin and Greek, and the history of the first days of English printing would have been much less interesting.

Caxton produced altogether a hundred books, ninety-seven of them at Westminster. Scarcely one of them does not

14. Caxton's device. Its meaning is the subject of controversy. It is suggested that the complex symbol between the large W and C is Caxton's mercer's mark, while the ornament before the W is an S and that after the C another C, the two standing for Sancta Colonae. This is adduced in support of the contention that Caxton learned printing in Cologne.

speak of the man who fathered it, either in a gently ironic prologue or epilogue—you must never go to read anything of Caxton's with too solemn a brow—or else in a mere phrase or a word at the end, as for example: 'Enprynted by Caxton in Feverer the colde season', which somehow says so much more than it shows, because the weather is irrelevant. Or there is a verse of two lines or more to send the book out into the world, with, as it were, something in its pocket. And then, as a matter of habit, the word 'Explicit', without which a Caxton is doubtfully a Caxton.

The great mark or device, whose meaning, if it has any at all, has aroused generations of speculation and comment, is not typical of a Caxton book, for it did not appear until 1487, and even then in a book, a Sarum missal, printed, not by Caxton, but for him by a Parisian printer. The last page of the book was blank, and on this Caxton printed his device, to emphasize that he was responsible for the work. The intertwined characters in the centre are possibly the mercer's mark with which Caxton used to stamp his bales of goods when he was of the Mercers' Company in Bruges.

Caxton never printed a Bible. It was as well that he did not try, for his business might easily have foundered under the expenses of so great a book; and no doubt he judged correctly that the demand for it was not large enough to repay the labour. He could only have published it in Latin, since no English translation yet existed, or might be allowed, and there were already enough Bibles in Latin and Greek to be had from foreign presses. Caxton's customers were the clergy, who wanted service books, psalters, and sermons, and Caxton supplied them; and the nobility and gentry, who wanted romances, of which a new one came regularly from the press at the sign of the Red Pale. Frequently it was a book of his own translation. It was while he was translating a book, or rather at the completion of it, that he died in 1491. The printing and publication of this last of Caxton's works was completed by Winkyn de Worde, who set at the end of it the words:

'Thus endyth the moost vertuous hystorye of the deuoute and right renowned lyves of the holy faders lyuinge in deserte, worthy of remembraunce to all wel dysposed persones which hath bē translated oute of Frenche into Englisshe by William Caxton of Westmynstre late deed and fynysshed at the laste daye of his lyffe.'

Explicit

WILLIAM CASLON

By the end of the seventeenth century the craft of printing had degenerated in England in every respect. Types were poor, paper was brownish and shoddy, and the work of the printer careless and tasteless. Although in this country printing had never reached the excellence of the best Continental printers, it had also never before fallen so low as it had by the year 1700. John Day in the sixteenth century was able to print books in a good roman type, which he probably cast himself, with far better alinement and far better press work than was general five or six generations later, when typefounding had become the work of the specialist and the printer was theoretically free to get on with his business of printing.

But he had not been free in another sense. For many years the printer had been under the rigid control of the Star Chamber, which strictly limited the numbers of printers and typefounders and always kept its eye upon the things they did, since there might be heresy in print, and treason also; the two might well be the same thing in a country where the sovereign was the head of the Church. The Star Chamber was there to preserve the right of the king and to protect him from danger, and in the free dissemination of printed matter the worthy gentlemen of the Chamber saw perhaps the most serious of all the enemies of privilege.

They were right in their belief; but such artificial restriction could not persist for ever in a nation rising to commercial power, and the Star Chamber was at last broken and annulled. The printer was set free of political control, but it was a freedom that was the heir of years of supervision, timidity, and lack of incentive.

47

Even its enemies would have needed a strong imagination then to see in the scrubby printing of England any inkling of the future power of the press. It was therefore enough of credit for a decent man to be dissatisfied with the standard of the time, and to work to improve it. Among men who thought so was William Bowyer, a printer of renown, who had his office in Dogwell Court in Whitefriars. Like other printers of his time, he depended on the foundries of Holland for his types, for even when type was bought through an English founder, such as Grover or James, it still came from Holland, the founders acting as middlemen only, or casting from Dutch matrices when they did cast type themselves. Bowyer was not satisfied with the state of his craft, and when he saw some letters on a book-binding which had been cut with 'uncommon neatness' he thought he saw the possibility of some improvement. He reasoned that a man who could cut the dies for the binder with such efficiency might be able to cut punches for a foundry equally well. He inquired who the brass-cutter was, and was directed to Mr. William Caslon, a young man not long out of his apprenticeship, who was making a living in a shop of his own in Vine Street, near the Minories. Caslon had learned the business of engraving and chasing the locks and barrels of guns, which in his time were often ornate and gave ample scope for the abilities of a fine artist. He also did engraving of other kinds, and on occasion would cut letters in brass for a binder.

It was this sideline of cutting letters that was to bring him to fame and fortune, through the offices of Mr. William Bowyer. The printer was evidently a man of perception, for he saw in the young engraver one who might become the mainspring of a new foundry which would give to England a competence in the manufacture of types which she lacked, and which might also give her independence of foreign foundries. He took Caslon on a visit to James's foundry in Bartholomew Close and showed him how types were made. The process was entirely new to Caslon, and no doubt he looked closely into every part of it, and remembered what he saw. He was asked if he could undertake the cutting of punches, and required a day to think the matter over. Perhaps he returned to his shop and put the question to a practical trial, for he came back at the end of the time and answered confidently that he could do it. Such caution, such modesty, and such confidence when confidence was justified seem to have been salient points of his character throughout his life. He was a careful man, and one who gained in dignity by being so.

Bowyer, together with two other printers, Bettenham and Watts, agreed to lend five hundred pounds to Caslon and this in itself shows the confidence they had in him even at so short acquaintance. The loan was made to enable Caslon to start a new foundry, and this he proceeded to do at once, choosing as his headquarters a garret in Helmet Row in Old Street. He must have spent some time in learning the technique of his new business, but there is no record of how he did this. He was evidently a good learner and gave such proofs of competence that in 1720 he was commissioned by the Society for the Promotion of Christian Knowledge to cut a new fount of arabic to be used in the printing of a New Testament and Psalter which the society intended to distribute in Palestine and Syria. Caslon produced a completely successful letter which gave pleasure to his patrons, and which was duly used in the books for which it was made.

Caslon published a specimen of his arabic, and placed his own name at the foot of it in capitals of a letter cut by himself. This, so the story goes, was seen by a printer called Palmer, who advised Caslon to continue and to cut the whole fount. There is no doubt at all that Caslon would have done this anyway, under the influence of Bowyer, and perhaps Palmer was merely an officious nobody advising where advice was not needed. In the event it rebounded on him, for he was in a position in which he dared not risk the ill will of other founders with whom he dealt, which now apparently gathered about his head, and he endeavoured to dissuade Caslon from the course which only a short while ago he had so earnestly recommended.

A few years later Caslon fell foul of the man again. Palmer was to print Bishop Hare's Hebrew Psalter, which was later published by Bowyer, and the Bishop objected to the use of the Hebrew types in Palmer's possession. He insisted on having Caslon's Hebrew types in his book and expected Palmer to get them. Palmer, however, was so deeply in debt to Caslon for goods he had already had that he did not dare to ask for more credit, and he had no ready money with which to buy type. Some new roman characters were also required for the book, for which punches would have to be cut. Palmer sought to relieve himself of the problem by representing to the Bishop that Caslon was an idle, dilatory man who would certainly keep them all waiting for years for the punches and the type. It would be much better, said Palmer, to make do with what he already had in his office, so that there should be no delay in the printing of the book. This did not satisfy the bishop, who sent for Bowyer to ask him about the character of Caslon. Bowyer gave a very different account of the founder, who was sent for in his turn. Caslon gave a date for the delivery of the material required, and the bishop found that he adhered to his promise.

Caslon was continuously busy cutting founts of roman and oriental characters and enlarging the business of his foundry, which had now become famous throughout the country and had already dealt a severe blow to the dominance of the Continental foundries in English printing. That dominance was soon destroyed for ever.

The letters he cut were not revolutionary, and were not intended to be so. There is no doubt at all that he took Dutch types as his models, and worked upon them by refining and improving and humanizing, until at last he had produced a letter as characteristic of English printing as any letter was to become, and which has been acclaimed by generations of printers and bibliophiles and typographers as one of the best and most readable of letters cut anywhere. Caslon, with a true eye and an accurate hand, was able to cut his punches with a correctness and delicacy and to aline his letters with an accuracy seldom to be found, and he set a technical standard which typefounders since have striven to maintain. Over several years he cut his letter in a full range of sizes so that the printer could depend on an English foundry for all his wants, and in addition he cut many flowers and ornaments to embellish the printer's page.

There is, unfortunately, no accurate record of the dates at which various types in Caslon's repertoire were cut, until his famous specimen sheet of 1734 was published. The date usually given for the foundation of his foundry is 1720, the year in which he was commissioned to cut the arabic for the Society for the Promotion of Christian Knowledge, but it does not seem likely that he would have been trusted with so important a commission in his first year of business. In the Caslon family there is a tradition that the business was founded in 1716, and this may be true. If so, there must certainly have been founts before the arabic, which equally certainly must have been romans. If this earlier date is accepted, the Palmer story becomes absurd unless it has been misplaced in time, and should have sprung from some incident other than the cutting of a row of initials at the foot of a specimen of arabic. Even so, it is difficult to believe that Bowyer, Watts, and Bettenham would not have been interested primarily in roman founts when they helped Caslon to found his business, and Caslon's first duties must have been to them. The conclusion is that by 1720 Caslon had already cut one or more of his roman founts and had made a reputation that attracted the work of cutting the arabic to him.

With the active backing of his three printers, not only in capital but as customers for the type he cast, and his own undoubted ability both as a craftsman and as a businessman, Caslon could not help but succeed, and he soon had to look for premises more convenient and more roomy than the garret in Helmet Row. He moved first to Ironmonger Row, where he did not stay long, but moved again to Chiswell Street, which is near the Barbican. Here he built the foundry which became famous throughout Europe and which continued on the same site for nearly two hundred years, until 1911, when the business was moved again—from one side of the street to the other. There it remained until 1936, when the stock was bought by Stephenson, Blake & Co., who thenceforward called their Sheffield works the Caslon Letter Foundry.

In Chiswell Street, in a building suited to his purpose,

A S P E C I M E N

By WILLIAM CASLON, Letter-Founder, in Chiswell-Street, LONDON.

DOUBLE PICA ROMAN.

Quoufque tandem abutere, Catilina, patientia noftra? quamdiu nos etiam furor ifte tuus eludet? quem ad finem fefe effrenata jactabit audacia? nihilne te
ABCDEFGHJIKLMNOP

GREAT PRIMER ROMAN.

Quoufque tandem abutere, Catilina, patientia noftra? quamdiu nos etiam furor ifte tuus eludet? quem ad finem fe fe effrenata jactabit audacia? nihilne te nocturnum præfidium palatii, nihil urbis vigiliæ, nihil timor populi, nihil conbis vigiliæ, nihil timor populi, nihil conABCDEFGHIJKLMNOPQRS

ENGLISH ROMAN.

Quoufque tandem abutere, Catilina, patientia noftra? quamdiu nos etiam furor ifte tuus eludet? quem ad finem fefe effrenata jactabit audacia? nihilne te nocturnum præfidium palatii, nihil confenfus urbis vigiliæ, nihil timor populi, nihil confenfus bonorum omnium, nihil hic munitiffimus ABCDEFGHIJKLMNOPQRSTVUW

PICA ROMAN.

Melium, noviſ rebus ſtudentem, manu ſua occidit. Fuit, fuit iſta quondam in hac repub. virtus, ut viri fortes acrioribus fuppliciis civem perniciofam, quam acerbiffimum hoftem coërcerent. Habemus enim fenatufconfultum in te, Catilina, vehemens, & grave: non deeſt reip. confilium, neque auctoritas hujus ordinis: nos, nos, dico aperte, confules defumus. De

Double Pica Italick.

Quoufque tandem abutere, Catilina, patientia noftra? quamdiu nos etiam furor ifte tuus eludet? quem ad finem fefe effrenata jacquem ad finem fefe effrenata jacABCDEFGHFJIKLMNO

Great Primer Italick.

Quoufque tandem abutere, Catilina, patientia noftra? quamdiu nos etiam furor ifte tuus eludet? quem ad finem fefe effrenata jactabit audacia? nibilne te nocturnum præfidium palatii, nibil urbis vigiliæ, nibil timor populi, nibil conABCDEFGHIJYKLMNOPQR

Englifh Italick.

Quoufque tandem abutere, Catilina, patientia noftra? quamdiu nos etiam furor ifte tuus eludet? quem ad finem fefe effrenata jactabit audacia? nibilne te nocturnum præfidium palatii, nibil confenfus bonorum omnium, nibil hic munitiffimus habendi fenorum omnium, nibil hic munitiffimus habendi feABCDEFGHIJKLMNOPQRSTVU

Pica Italick.

Melium, novis rebus ftudentem, manu fua occidit. Fuit, fuit ifta quondam in hac repub. virtus, ut viri fortes acrioribus fuppliciis civem perniciofam, quam acerbiffimum boftem coërcerent. Habemus enim fenatufconfultum in te, Catilina, vehemens, & grave: non deeft reip. confilium, neque auctoritas bujus ordinis: nos, nos, dico aperte, confules defumus. Derrori quondam fenatu

Pica Black.

And be it further enacted by the Authority afozefaid, That all and every of the faid Exchequer Bills to be made forth by virtue of this Act, oz to many of them as ſhall from A B C D E F G H I L M D D P Q R S E

Brevier Black.

And be it further enacted by the Authozity afozeſaid. That all and every of the faid Exchequer Bills to be made forth by virtue of this Act, oz to many of them as ſhall from time to time remain undiſcharged of the ſaid ſum of fourteen hundzed thouſand pounds, and alſo all and every the Bills and every the Bills oz Debentures, ſmall oz Debentures, ſmall

Pica Gothick.

ATTA NNSAK ÞN IN HUMINAM VEIÞVAI NAMÞ ÞEIN UMAI ÞIÞNAINASSNS ÞEINS VAIKÞAI VIAÞA ÞEINS SVE IN HUMINA

Pica Coptick.

ϩⲉⲛ ⲟⲩⲁⲣⲭⲏ ⲁϥⲧ ⲉⲙⲙⲟ ⲓⲧⲧϣⲉ ⲛⲉⲁⲙ ⲛⲕⲁϫⲓⲛ ⲡⲓⲕⲁϫⲓ ϫⲉ ⲛⲉ ⲟⲩⲁⲗⲁⲧ ⲉⲡⲟϥ ⲛⲉ ⲟⲧⲟϩ ⲁⲩⲧⲟⲟϥⲧ ⲟⲩϫⲁⲕⲓ ⲛⲁϫⲓⲭⲛ ⲉϫⲉⲛ ϥⲛⲟⲩⲛ ⲟⲩⲟϩ ⲟⲩⲛⲁ ⲛⲧⲉϥⲧ ⲛⲁϫⲛⲟⲟⲣ ⲉⲭⲉⲛ ⲛⲓⲙⲱⲟⲩ ϯ ⲟ-

Pica Armenian.

Սկսբն Ընարածրեայ երե՛ա՛լ և Ֆրմքութիֆ զիժ ֆեֆ․ և զդքֆերեֆ երար, ժ․ զ Ֆֆֆ ֆֆֆ ՖՖ ֆֆ ֆֆ զֆ Ֆֆֆֆֆֆ նֆ ֆֆֆֆֆֆֆֆ զ Ֆֆֆֆֆֆ

Englifh Syriack.

ܘܒܪܫܝܬ ܐܝܬܘܗܝ ܗܘܐ ܡܠܬܐ ܘܗܘ ܡܠܬܐ ܐܝܬܘܗܝ ܗܘܐ ܠܘܬ ܐܠܗܐ ܘܐܠܗܐ ܐܝܬܘܗܝ ܗܘܐ ܗܘ ܡܠܬܐ

Pica Samaritan.

ﬔﬕﬓﬔﬕﬖﬔﬕ ﬔﬕﬓﬔﬕﬓ ﬔﬕﬓﬔﬕﬓ ﬔﬕﬓﬔﬕﬓﬔﬕ

ABCD

French Cannon.

Quoufque tandem abutere, Catilina, pati-

Quouſque tandem

ABCDE

ABCDEFG

ABCDEFGHI

ABCDEFGHIJK

ABCDEFGHIJKL

ABCDEFGHIKLMN

15. Caslon's specimen sheet of 1734 showing the range of his types, together with black letter and exotic founts.

Caslon organized his expanding business. He must have had a considerable staff, including several casters, finishers, boys to break off the tangs, and people to pack the types in founts, besides labourers to handle the heavy type metal and to keep the furnaces hot and the crucibles full. The casters were deployed against one wall, each with his own cubicle formed by a wood partition separating him from his fellow on either side, with, before him, his furnace and crucible of lead, and a table for the type, and above his head a shelf with a box for matrices. In his left hand the man held a mould with a long spring holding the matrix in position in it. Molten metal was poured in the mould orifice, and then the workman would make a sudden upward jerk designed to force the metal into the furthest corners of the mould—an effort which has sometimes been described as like an antic of some grotesque dance. The mould was then opened and the letter ejected. It was cast with a tang or projection, which was the surplus lead, and this was broken off by boys. Each letter was then rubbed by another workman to give it a clean finish, and then dressed by another man. There is in existence a print of Caslon's foundry in 1750 which shows these operations in progress. The rubber and the dresser in this print are Joseph Jackson and Thomas Cottrell, two men who were themselves to start business as letter-founders later.

The cutting of punches Caslon reserved for himself. This was the most skilled and the most difficult of all processes in letter-founding, and it was not a task that could be delegated by a man who was himself an artist in letter forms and wished to have exactly a particular kind of letter. Caslon did the work in his own quarters, but not, apparently, to keep any secret, for he was seen at work both by Jackson and Cottrell, who evidently learned by watching him, and put their observations to good use when they began on their own account.

Outside his business Caslon was devoted to music. No doubt a performer himself, though on what is not known, he shared his pleasure with many friends, and gathered them together for a monthly meeting and concert at his house. He may have done this as early as his days in Helmet Row,

54

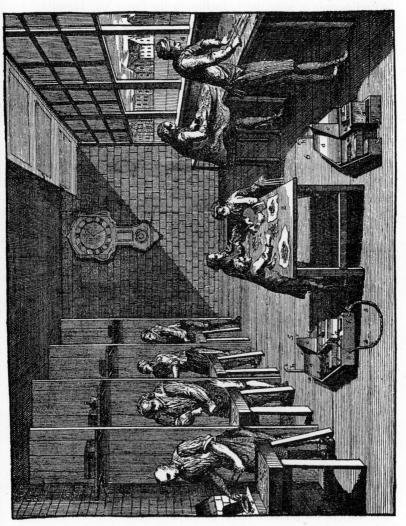

16. William Caslon's foundry in 1750. On the left are the casters, each in his booth, with his furnace, crucible, ladle, and rat-tail mould; on the right, before the large windows, are the dressers, finishing the types, while in the centre are boys who will take away the finished type for packing.

but by the time he came to Chiswell Street his friends numbered many important people, and it was not surprising to find people of note there, including the great Mr. Handel himself, come to talk in his German-English and perhaps to play on the organ a part of a new oratorio. These meetings were timed for a night of the full moon, so that the friends might find it easier to walk through the streets on their way home. From this pleasant custom they came to call themselves the Luna-ticks.

Caslon was universally respected, both as a citizen and as a craftsman, and he enjoyed life without setback. So even was the tenor of it that there were in fact few incidents that left their marks in men's memories or in their records, and Caslon's life therefore is particularly difficult to recount. If, at the same time as he had been a successful founder, he had also been a brawling, contentious scoundrel, we would have known more of him and would have found it easier to bring him alive in a book; for the extraordinary and worthless character is remembered where the worthy citizen is forgotten.

There is only one example of Caslon's failing to perceive advantage in a commercial undertaking, and only this one example, if indeed it is so, of his failure to observe the strictest of honour. About 1725 an Edinburgh goldsmith, William Ged, invented a method of reproducing a page of type in the manner we now call stereotyping, and he sought capital and interest from various founders and printers. A company was formed, including Thomas James, the founder, one of Caslon's rivals in London. As a member of the company, James was naturally asked to supply the type for the purpose of Ged's demonstrations. Perhaps he was from the first secretly antagonistic to this method of reproducing letters which seemed to reduce the demand for types, or perhaps he was at first favourable and later changed his mind; but anyway, he sent to Ged type that was worn and battered and which would not have given a good result however well it was reproduced. Ged rejected the type and went to a printer who had, he knew, founts of type from Caslon's foundry. This printer asked Caslon for his opinion. Caslon at once denied the utility of the invention and asserted that

56

he could, anyway, practise the process as well or better than Ged. Ged took Caslon up on this and a wager of £50 was arranged. Caslon and Ged were each given a page of type and allowed eight days to produce duplicates. Ged produced three duplicates in one day before Caslon had done anything, and Ged was therefore acclaimed the winner.

On the strength of this victory over the redoubted Caslon, Ged and his friends got a contract from the University of Cambridge to print Bibles and Prayer Books by their new method. James and his cronies were not beaten, however; they conspired to spoil the work and discredit it. The compositors made errors in the typesetting and the pressmen used their ink balls with too much force, so that the plates were damaged. Probably the compositors in the printing house were themselves involved, because they saw in this new invention something that reduced the amount of composition necessary—for by its aid two or more formes of a page of type might be made so that two or more copies of the page might be printed at once, or so many different presses be set to work together on the same book, which otherwise, when such multiple printing was required, had all to be set up in duplicate by hand. Such animosities were not uncommon later in the century and in the next one, when the great mechanization of industry began. Feelings were strong enough to persuade the authorities to suppress the books, and the plates were sent eventually to Caslon's foundry to be broken up and melted down.

However this episode is regarded, Caslon does not come well out of it. It may be that he shared James's obstructionist ideas because he saw in the invention something that threatened the foundry he had so carefully built up and which was still comparatively young, and if this is the case he is all the more to be condemned. Financially, however, except for his fifty pounds, he came out of it unscarred. The wretched James suffered differently. The printers who had fought against the invention remembered James's connection with it and henceforth would not buy from him, and no doubt the business that he lost Caslon gained.

Ged, broken in health and fortune, returned to Edinburgh,

and the world had to wait for the rediscovery of a process that has been of infinite service to it.

Caslon was married three times, his first wife being Sarah Pearman. They had two sons and a daughter. One of the sons, also William, joined his father in the foundry, and learned the business so thoroughly that he began to take over many of the duties that his father had hitherto performed, so that life was made easier for the older man. Eventually the elder Caslon retired from the business altogether to leave his son in charge, and went to live first in the Hackney Road, then at Water Gruel Row, and finally to a country house at Bethnal Green. There, at seventy-four, he died in 1766.

Perhaps before he died he understood something of the forces that were then active in the world of type and which would eventually obscure his beloved letter and drive it out of use for many years. Baskerville's work he must have known, though there is no record of his opinion of it—indeed there is no record of his opinion of anything; and on the Continent Bodoni and the Didots were moving in a direction away from everything Caslon had stood for. Within forty years of his death his type was overwhelmed, and the markets full of modern faces vastly inferior to anything he had done, but none the less victorious. Caslon's type remained lost, but for a venture here and a sally there, until the composing machine companies brought it back in this century, which may well be described as the era of the old face.

JOHN BASKERVILLE

I N the first half of the eighteenth century Birmingham
was already a notable manufacturing town, and it had
been for a hundred years or more. It was famous for
the number of its smithies and the many kinds of metal
goods produced in them. Invention and enterprise were not
novelties in the town, and the rather odd and certainly
extraordinary young man who arrived there about 1725 to
make his fortune was no lonely star come to brighten a sullen
dark. The firmament of Birmingham was already scattered
with sturdy lights that shone with independence and bright
prosperity. Nevertheless, this newcomer, obscure at his
arrival, was one day to shine with a new sort of lustre in the
town that, then as now, concentrated so purposefully upon
matters of business.

John Baskerville came of a family that had lived at Sion
Hill, in Wolverley, near Kidderminster, for generations. His
parents do not seem to have been rich, but they were
evidently able to give their son a reasonable education. That
education would normally have included instruction in writing, and the young Baskerville must have proved a ready
and rewarding pupil, for he was from an early age in love
with the shapes of letters, and this interest persisted throughout his life. He soon became expert, so much so that at the
age of nineteen he felt himself able to teach writing. At that
age, in 1725, he came to Birmingham to set up as a writing
master.

He was not likely to make a fortune by this enterprise, but
it served to earn him a living and put to good use a skill he
undoubtedly possessed. Later he joined to this business of
teaching, another, that of cutting inscriptions in stone. As an

advertisement for this, he engraved a slab of slate, and stood it in his window, or fixed it outside his door. It announced: 'Gravestones cut in any of the hands by John Baskerville, Writing Master.' The five lines are cut in five different kinds of letter—to show his versatility, no doubt—two kinds of gothic, 'Baskerville' capitals and lower case, 'Baskerville' italic capitals, and the word 'By' in a copperplate script; the whole surrounded by graceful interlacing flourishes. It is a handsome stone, and it still exists, preserved in the public library at Birmingham.

For ten years Baskerville pursued these twin avocations, with what prosperity there might be in them, but there is no doubt that he sought to make his fortune. Why else should he have come the fifteen miles from Wolverley to the metropolis of Birmingham? He knew what he wanted, and what he meant to do when the opportunity arose. Despite his flourishes and his dandyism, which he perhaps affected already, he was essentially a practical man, and he sought a practical business.

As he approached the thirtieth year of his life a fashion arose in England for a new kind of ornamental ware called japan. The japanning process is a method of decorating a wide variety of articles, from buttons to tea trays, which are covered and protected by a layer of glossy varnish, stoved hard in ovens. This manufacture attracted the writing master, and about 1740 he set himself up in business in it.

A rival manufacturer, Taylor, was already at work, using mass-production methods and child labour that are more typical of the nineteenth century than the eighteenth. From what may be judged of Baskerville's character, it does not seem likely that he could have adopted these methods. Throughout his life he showed himself persistent in the pursuit of excellence, and Taylor's methods could scarcely have led in that direction. Baskerville's certainly did, for he soon became notable for the quality and the fine design of his goods. So much was this so, that people who came to see him later, when he had turned printer and become famous, came as much to see the manufacture of japan as to view the manufacture of books. It was a profitable enterprise. In ten

V. BIRMINGHAM

THE SOU'

ᴋERVILLE KNEW IT

ᴘECT IN 1731

years Baskerville was independent, and for the rest of his life japanning kept him in comfort and affluence. It enabled him to pursue his hobby of printing, which, however glorious, did not prove a financial success.

He was always proud of his work, both as a japanner and as a printer, and well he might be, for here, if ever there was one, was a characteristic Birmingham product—the self-made man. He considered his goods superlative, and very likely they were; he thought that 'their beauty without violence would not be impaired in several ages'. Alas, of all the thousands of trays and ornaments and decorated ware that must have come from his workshop throughout the thirty or forty years of its existence, not one example survives today, not one. The hard-stoved wood and steel have vanished; and yet his books remain, perishable paper, out-lasting what should be far more perdurable materials.

His continuing prosperity enabled Baskerville to buy a piece of property just outside the town, and to build there a house which he called Easy Hill. Contemporary illustrations show it as a square and not particularly handsome building, with little of the eighteenth-century grace of architecture. In it Baskerville was to spend the rest of his life, and presumably to find room there for his japanning and printing enterprises.

By this time he had become a person of importance in the town, a worthy citizen, respected for his ability and his prosperity, but perhaps a little amusing for his lavish dress of green and gold and for the elaborate and expensive carriage in which he would drive about Birmingham and the surrounding districts. Some people thought him absurd and a coxcomb, and ridiculed his pretensions to taste and culture, to philosophy and the arts. He was not, however, a person to be taken lightly. He knew his mind, he was strong of will, and his energy was persistent. He was independent to excess and seems to have cared little what people thought of him and of his actions.

This independence of spirit is illustrated in the affair of Sarah Eaves. Mrs. Eaves was a wife of a forger, Richard Eaves, who had fled abroad to escape the law, and had left his wife with four children to look after and very little means. Baskerville took pity on her and brought her to his new house at Easy Hill, with her children—or at least two of them. She became his housekeeper; but they soon began to live together as man and wife, and he somehow made the world think of her as his wife, with a surprising absence of scandal. He took the children to him as affectionately as though they had been his own—indeed, one of the boys he destined for his heir. In this way John and Sarah lived as man and wife for sixteen years, until the death of Richard Eaves in 1764 allowed them to marry—a ceremony which, I imagine, John Baskerville regarded as of little importance and suffered only for the sake of Sarah. It was a good and contented partnership. Sarah was evidently a good manager who was able to keep house efficiently and comfortably, and who was also practical enough to be able to play a part in the management of the japanning business—I suspect that later, when her husband became immersed in printing, Sarah did most of the managing of the japan side.

Baskerville's importance as a citizen of Birmingham was increasing. He had already held minor public offices of the kind that worthy citizens might be asked to discharge, but in 1764 he was appointed High Bailiff, the principal position of authority under the manorial system by which the town was governed at that time. He seems to have acquitted himself with competence. It was part of the responsibility of this office to see that peace and honest dealing were maintained—he was responsible, for example, for the correction of weights and measures used by merchants and dealers. In one of the local newspapers a notice was inserted over his name, asking the people to observe fair dealings, not to deal in calumny, and not to damage a person's credit by idle gossip. It is possible that he had himself suffered in this way because of gossip; certainly he did so suffer later, for another notice in a newspaper announced that, despite rumours to the contrary, John Baskerville was able to pay all his debts in cash, and at sight.

It was not until 1750, when he was forty-four years old, that Baskerville decided to become a printer. It is not clear

Rothwell ſc

17. John Baskerville, from an engraving in the Birmingham Public Library.

what it was that underlay this decision, but having taken it, he pursued it with characteristic energy, tenacity, and persistence. Persistence is a word that describes all Baskerville's efforts in the field of printing. He did not work quickly; on the contrary, he worked with a methodical thoroughness that was sometimes the despair of those who came to be associated with him in the production of books. He would be at a task for months and years that another printer would accomplish in a quarter or a tenth of the time.

He began, of course, with a great deal to learn. Printing has never been a business that could be picked up in a matter of weeks, and Baskerville did not set out to be only a printer. He could have bought his types ready made from the foundry of William Caslon, or some other foundry, and he could have had his presses made for him by those who manufactured such things. He could have bought his ink, too, and his paper, and all the things needed to produce the printed sheet and the bound book. Instead he chose to make many of them himself. He wanted to print in his own way with letters of his own design and founding, and he wanted accurate and efficient presses which he knew he could make but which could not be bought from elsewhere. All this meant, in effect, a return to that manner of commencing printer which had been the custom in the childhood of the art. Then a man must cut his own punches, strike his own matrices, cast his own type, and make his own ink—all these before he could start to print a line. Baskerville did not, of course, do all these things with his own hands—no man could have done so, and certainly not one who, like Baskerville, sought perfection in the smallest detail and was willing to scrap hours of work and to start again because the result did not satisfy him; but all these things were done on his premises and to his instruction and with his active intervention.

His presses were constructed to a degree of precision beyond anything normally available. It was evidently his intention that mechanical imperfections in the tools of printing should not be allowed to hinder or affect the perfection of the printed page. For example, he boasts that for the platens of his presses, the surface that applies pressure to squeeze the paper against the type, he used brass an inch thick, where others used wood or slate, and that these plates of brass were ground to so accurate a surface that they would adhere together—by suction, he means, as perfectly flat surfaces will adhere. He had some special means of producing an accurate surface, which he needed in japanning and for which he had applied for a patent eight years earlier. Such precision is necessary for the efficient operation of a press, as modern manufacturers know, but it was not the common practice or standard of the ordinary manufacturer of that time. A printing press is designed to apply a considerable force of pressure, but to apply it evenly and steadily, so that the pressure on any particular letter is only just sufficient to impart the ink to the paper. It is, of course, not likely that Baskerville's presses were as accurate as a modern press, but they must have been a great improvement on the ordinary press of his time.

He was particular about the quality of his black printing ink. A fault of books of the period, in general, is the greyness of the ink, and Baskerville was determined that this fault should not characterize his books. He therefore sought a black of deep, rich quality, and to this end contrived a formula of lampblack and varnishes which satisfied him. The mixture had to mature for a long period—years, in fact—before it was really ready for use. Baskerville would have learned something of the mixing of pigments and varnishes in his business as a japanner, and no doubt he found that knowledge of service when he came to make printing ink, which, it should be understood, has more the consistency of paint than of ordinary writing ink. Baskerville enhanced the quality of his black by treating the paper after printing, pressing it between plates of hot copper to give the paper and the ink a sheen or gloss.

Baskerville is also credited at times with the manufacture of his own paper, but it is unlikely that he made it for his books. He certainly experimented with paper, and he may have been responsible for the introduction of wove paper. Before his day paper was commonly laid, that is to say, it bore the marks of the stronger wires that supported the mesh in the deckle or sieve of the paper-maker. Such paper is still made and can be identified at once by holding it up to the light, when the structure of parallel lines is clear. Wove paper is made in a rather different manner, and does not show any of these lines. It therefore has a smoother surface, a characteristic that suited Baskerville very well.

Although he did not make paper for his books, there is no doubt at all that Baskerville made paper of another kind, writing paper. He invented a kind of paper with a smooth semi-translucent surface, which resembled vellum, and marketed it through the bookseller Dodsley in London; but he made far too much, so that Dodsley had to beg him to stop sending consignments, and had even to send quantities of it back to Birmingham. This enthusiasm is only one example of that curious lack of business acumen that was frequently exhibited, in printing, by the successful Birmingham business man.

Baskerville's types were made at Easy Hill. The punches for them were cut by John Handy, who joined Baskerville about 1750, and thenceforward probably cut all the punches made for the printing house there. Handy proved an excellent workman who was able to cut his employer's letter designs without taint of the prevailing old-face style. From Handy's punches matrices were struck, and from these in turn the type was cast. This was the slowest and most painstaking of all the processes Baskerville chose to operate for the production of his books. Punch-cutting is tedious and minutely detailed work, and a man might well be engaged for two or three days in cutting one letter, particularly when there is at his elbow a perfectionist like Baskerville, ready to scrap the work and to start all over again, several times if necessary. A fount of type includes capitals and lower-case, figures and small capitals, and points of punctuation—a hundred or more characters for the roman alone in each size required. It should be no wonder that years went by before Baskerville was ready to print; but he was, in the event, longer than one might reasonably have expected.

Baskerville was acquainted with William Shenstone, who lived at the Leasowes, near Birmingham. Shenstone was well known as a poet, but he had become even better known as a landscape gardener, and he had made of the Leasowes, which he had inherited in 1745, a showplace famous as far away as London. Shenstone took a good deal of interest in the progress of the press in Birmingham and was always ready with advice on literary and artistic matters. He introduced Baskerville to Dodsley, the bookseller and publisher, and these two, the printer and the publisher, came to some kind of understanding about the publication of the future products of the Baskerville press. More than that, they became firm and fast friends.

There were not yet, however, any books to be published. If progress was methodical, it was also exceedingly protracted, and sometimes it seemed merely dilatory to Dodsley. The correspondence between them contains many pleas and urgings from Dodsley, and in answer to them only occasional announcements of minor triumphs from Baskerville. In 1752 he sent Dodsley a specimen sheet showing only fourteen characters of two-line great primer, 'to remove in some measure your impatience'. In a footnote he added: 'Pray put it in no one's power to let Mr. Caslon see them.' They were, he said, about to set about thirteen italic characters, which would be completed in a fortnight.

It is interesting that Baskerville should have wished to keep his type face secret from Caslon, the most notable of the English founders.

The first book from the new press was to be a fine edition of Virgil's works. In 1753 Dodsley was advertising it and inviting orders and subscriptions, evidently in the belief that it would shortly be ready for publication. But it was not ready that year; nor the year after. In that following year Baskerville was still writing about the production of the types. The great primer was finished at last, and progress was being made with english, a two-line double pica, and a two-line small pica.

It was four years since Baskerville had decided to become a printer, four years in which work had been done but in which

67

PUBLII VIRGILII
MARONIS
BUCOLICA
GEORGICA
ET
AENEIS

Ad optimorum Exemplarium fidem recensita.

TO THE PUBLIC.

JOHN BASKERVILLE proposes, by the advice and assistance of several learned men, to print, from the Cambridge edition corrected with all possible care, an elegant edition of Virgil. The work will be printed in quarto, on this writing royal paper, and with the letter annex'd. The price of the volume in sheets will be one guinea, no part of which will be required till the book is delivered. It will be put to press as soon as the number of Subscribers shall amount to five hundred whose names will be prefixt to the work. All persons who are inclined to encourage the undertaking, are desired to send their names to JOHN BASKERVILLE in Birmingham; who will give specimens of the work to all who are desirous of seeing them.

Subscriptions are also taken in, and specimens delivered by Messieurs R. and
J. DODSLEY, Booksellers in Pall Mall, London. MDCCLIV.

18. A specimen page issued by Baskerville i

P. *VIRGILII MARONIS*

BUCOLICA

ÉCLOGA I. cui nomen *TITYRUS.*

M E L I B OE U S, T I T Y R U S.

Tityre, tu patulæ recubans fub tegmine fagi,
    Silveftrem tenui Mufam meditaris avena:
Nos patriæ fines, et dulcia linquimus arva,
Nos patriam fugimus: tu Tityre lentus in umbra
Formofam refonare doces Amaryllida filvas.
T. O Melibœe, Deus nobis hæc otia fecit:
Namque erit ille mihi femper Deus; illius aram
Sæpe tener noftris ab ovilibus imbuet agnus:
Ille meas errare boves, ut cernis, et ipfum
Ludere quæ vellem, calamo permifit agrefti.
M. Non equidem invideo; miror magis: undique totis
Ufque adeo turbatur agris. en ipfe capellas
Protenus æger ago: hanc etiam vix Tityre duco.
Hic inter denfas corylos modo namque gemellos,
Spem gregis, ah! filice in nuda connixa reliquit.
Sæpe malum hoc nobis, fi mens non læva fuiffet,
De cœlo taĉtas memini prædicere quercus.
Sæpe finiftra cava prædixit ab ilice cornix.
Sed tamen, ifte Deus qui fit, da, Tityre, nobis.
T. Urbem, quam dicunt Romam, Melibœe, putavi
Stultus ego huic noftræ fimilem, quo fæpe folemus
Paftores ovium teneros depellere fœtus.
Sic canibus catulos fimiles, fic matribus hædos
Noram; fic parvis componere magna folebam.

as a prospectus for his edition of Virgil.

nothing had been produced for sale. Such an expenditure of time means also an expenditure of money. Despite his wealth, Baskerville could not help but notice that printing under these conditions was becoming an expense of some magnitude. There had been wages to pay all this time, and the cost of materials, varnish, metals, paper, and so forth for a large book now undoubtedly in course of production and locking up more and more capital as it progressed. A few customers for the printing house would be an advantage, and Baskerville went to London in 1755 almost certainly with the intention of persuading some of the booksellers to employ his press—the booksellers were also the publishers in his day. He had little success. He may have quoted prices that frightened them away, for it is known that, later, the prices he charged were greatly in excess of those of other printers—two and even three times as much. Further, his type face was not universally popular when at last it appeared in a book, and it is possible that when he showed his specimens he met with setbacks and adverse comments.

But he was not a man to be put off by anyone's opinion. He may have been hurt and disappointed that his types were not received with immediate acclaim, but he would not therefore change his letters to please the booksellers. If they would not come to him, then he would do without them, for his ambitious mind was filled with other things, other adventures in printing in which his types would show to advantage. He wanted to print an edition of the works of Milton, and above all he wanted to print a Bible and a Prayer Book. He could not print any of these without getting permission from someone. The booksellers claimed all rights in English authors as far back as Shakespeare; and certain privileged holders of the right to print the Bible and the Prayer Book claimed copyright in perpetuity. One of these bodies was the University of Cambridge, and in 1756 Baskerville went to Cambridge no doubt to obtain the permission he wanted.

In this same year he wrote to Dodsley in London to say that the Virgil would be ready in the following January. Perhaps Dodsley no longer took these promises seriously, but when April came and still no Virgil, he thought it time to complain once more of the delay, and did so. However, the book really was on the point of completion, and soon afterwards it was published, four years after Dodsley's first advertisement announcing it, and seven years after Baskerville had started printing. It was the first fruit of his press.

The effect of the publication of the book was remarkable. Though Baskerville's style owed something to that of the Scottish printers, the Virgil was none the less an original achievement, distinct from contemporary work; and of course there was the new type, now for the first time to be seen in a book. Because it was new and different the book excited either marked aversion or admiration. Among the connoisseurs Baskerville found himself notable immediately. Not all of them may have liked the book, but no one of taste and knowledge could deny that here was evidence of infinite care and labour, of skilful printing, and of superbly competent design. Those who disliked the book did so for reasons that puzzle us now. The type caused particular objection. There were complaints that it was dazzling and painful to the eye, and allegations that constant reading of it would make the reader blind. This sort of nonsense hampered Baskerville— or rather, arose about his works—throughout his life. A great deal of it was prejudice, and much of it was prejudice founded on complete lack of knowledge and taste, a kind of following of a fashion to belittle Baskerville. His friends encountered it everywhere, and Benjamin Franklin, who understood and appreciated Baskerville's genius, wrote to him of one such experience:

'Let me give you a pleasant instance of the prejudice some have entertained against your work,' he said. 'Soon after I returned, discoursing with a gentleman concerning the artists of Birmingham, he said you would be the means of blinding all the readers of the nation, for the strokes of your letters, being too thin and narrow, hurt the eye, and he could never read a line of them without pain. "I thought," said I, "you were going to complain of the gloss on the paper some object to." "No, no," said he. "I have heard that mentioned, but it is not that; it is the form and cut of the letters themselves, they have not that height and thickness of the stroke which

11 ¶ Oh, thou afflicted, toffed with tempeft, *and* not comforted, behold, I will lay thy ftones with ⁿ fair colours, and lay thy foundations with fapphires.

12 And I will make thy windows of agates, and thy gates of carbuncles, and all thy borders of pleafant ftones.

11 ¶ Oh, thou afflicted, toffed with tempeft, *and* not comforted, behold, I will lay thy ftones with ⁿ fair colours, and lay thy foundations with fapphires.

12 And I will make thy windows of agates, and thy gates of carbuncles, and all thy borders of pleafant ftones.

19. Caslon's type compared with Baskerville's.

make the common printing so much more comfortable to the eye." You see, this gentleman was a connoisseur. In vain I endeavoured to support your character against the charge; he knew what he felt and could see the reason for it, and several other gentlemen among his friends had made the same observation, etc. Yesterday he called to visit me, when, mischievously bent to try his judgement, I stepped into my closet, tore off the top of Mr. Caslon's specimen, and produced it to him as yours, brought with me from Birmingham, saying, I had been examining it since he spoke to me, and could not for the life of me see that disproportion he mentioned, desiring him to point it out to me. He readily undertook it, and went over the several founts, showing me everywhere what he thought instances of that disproportion; and declared that he could not then read the specimen without feeling very strongly the pain he had mentioned to me. I spared him that time the confusion of being told that these were the types he had been reading all his life, with so much ease to his eyes; the types his adored Newton is printed with, on which he has pored not a little; nay the very types his own book is printed with (for he is himself an author), and yet never discovered the painful disproportion in them, til he thought they were yours.'

This frequent complaint of the thinness of the types is a curious one, for the general feel of a page of Baskerville, set in a manner comparable to that of a page of Caslon, is that the Baskerville type is the heavier and the sturdier of the two, and it is hard to see how anyone could have complained of the legibility of the characters. Baskerville's printing, too, was better than that of the majority of printers, and that also was an advantage towards legibility.

The importance of Baskerville's letters lies in their tendency towards a new kind of design, different from that of the prevailing old face, exemplified in England by Caslon. Baskerville's characters show the modification of the stress nearer to the vertical—this is shown most clearly in the O, in which the thinnest strokes are directly north and south of the centre. Old face letters have the thinnest strokes north-north-west and south-south-east. This slanting stress is not typical of all old faces—some of Caslon's letters are as upright as Baskerville's—but the vertical shading is typical of all modern faces. Baskerville's letter was a transitional design between the two kinds. The stress is a little heavier, and the thick strokes change into thin ones, as in the O, more abruptly. The serifs, particularly on the ascenders, are straighter and more delicately bracketed, and sharper at their terminations. The general effect is that of a letter more precisely conceived and drawn, with the beginnings of that sharpness and rigidity that come from the engraver rather than from the pen. That is indeed the difference between the old face and the modern letter—the first, at whatever remove, is still based upon the custom and habit of the pen, while the modern face derives from the limitations and characteristics of engraving.

73

Baskerville was not the kind of man to be deterred by the criticisms of booksellers or others who disliked him, and he was certainly not to be turned from his work by the animadversions of those who spoke of him as an upstart Birmingham manufacturer thrusting himself into regions of taste and culture in which he was a stranger. He pursued his course steadily, and was soon immersed in the production of the edition of Milton's works, for which he must have come to an agreement with the booksellers who claimed the copyright. There were also the Bible and the Book of Common Prayer, the printing of which was always his ambition. He set up and printed specimen pages for the Prayer Book and sent them to Dodsley, with the remark that the size of the type was 'calculated for those who begin to want spectacles, but are ashamed to use them in church'.

The right to print the Bible and the Prayer Book were not gained easily. He had chosen to negotiate with the University of Cambridge, and the university drove a hard bargain. They demanded a payment of twenty pounds for each thousand copies of the Bible printed by Baskerville, and twelve pounds ten shillings per thousand for the Prayer Book; in addition he had to pay thirty-two pounds to the Stationers' Company for the right to add the Psalms in metre to the Prayer Book.

The privilege of printing these books apparently carried with it the honorary office of printer to the university, and it apparently also implied that the printing must be done at Cambridge. Baskerville shipped off two presses, type, and other necessary material, and sent with it Thomas Warren, as his assistant and representative, to oversee the production of the books. Baskerville himself does not seem to have gone to live in Cambridge, though it must be assumed that he made frequent journeys there during the progress of the work. It seems odd that he should have chosen to remain in Birmingham while his most important work was proceeding a hundred miles away. The posts and transport of the eighteenth century were not rapid and must have been responsible for numerous delays and exasperations.

At home at Easy Hill Baskerville got on with the printing

74

PARADISE LOST.

BOOK II.

HIGH on a throne of royal ſtate, which far
    Outſhone the wealth of Ormus and of Ind,
Or where the gorgeous eaſt with richeſt hand
Show'rs on her kings barbaric pearl and gold,
Satan exalted ſat, by merit rais'd   5
To that bad eminence; and from deſpair
Thus high uplifted beyond hope, aſpires
Beyond thus high, inſatiate to purſue
Vain war with Heav'n, and by ſucceſs untaught
His proud imaginations thus diſplay'd.   10
    Pow'rs and Dominions, Deities of Heaven,
For ſince no deep within her gulf can hold
Immortal vigor, though oppreſs'd and fall'n,
I give not Heav'n for loſt. From this deſcent
Celeſtial virtues riſing, will appear   15
More glorious and more dread than from no fall,
And truſt themſelves to fear no ſecond fate.
Me though juſt right, and the fix'd laws of Heaven
Did firſt create your leader, next free choice,
With what beſides, in counſel or in fight,   20
Hath been achiev'd of merit, yet this loſs
                            Thus

20. The opening page of Book II of *Paradise Lost,* one of Baskerville's
most satisfying books.

of the Milton. This book, a quarto in four volumes, appeared on the market in 1758, another fine piece of typographical virtuosity that added, among the discerning, yet more to its designer's reputation. The new printer was making his mark. And yet he was not such a very new printer by now, for he had been working for eight years, and his apprenticeship was surely over. Caxton, starting printing at the same age as Baskerville, printed more in two years than Baskerville did in eight. Only the Virgil and the Milton had appeared, and a start made at Cambridge on the Bible and the Prayer Book. It was really not very much for so long, however fine it was. It is little wonder that Baskerville complained so frequently of the cost of printing.

The edition of Milton was a success—if success is to be measured merely by the quantity sold. It was soon sold out and two more editions were printed in the two following years, but this time in two volumes only, at sixteen shillings the volume.

The first volume contains a preface by Baskerville in which he states his aims as a printer. 'It is not my desire', he said, 'to print many books, but only such as are books of consequence, of intrinsic merit, or established reputation, and which the public may be pleased to see in an elegant dress, and to purchase them at such a price as will repay the extraordinary care and expense that must necessarily be bestowed on them.' This was an intention that could deserve nothing but praise, but he was not always able to hold to it. In the books he printed at his own risk, he did hold to it; but he came to find printing so expensive a hobby that he was compelled to look for some way of winning back some of his money, and so he undertook the printing of books for private customers or booksellers, as any other printer did, for profit; some of these books are not well printed, and many of them have little merit. Unfortunately for the prosperity of his press, no large number of customers could be found to pay the high prices that Baskerville charged. No such defects, if he could help it, should mar the perfection of the books he printed for himself, and on which he could spend what time and effort he pleased. The Bible and the Prayer Book in particular were to be as fine as he could make them, the pinnacles of his achievement. The first specimen page of the Bible was sent to Cambridge in 1759, but there is no record of what the syndics of the press thought of it. The Prayer Book, as the lesser of the two tasks, was already well under way, indeed, at this time must have been approaching completion, for it was published in the spring of 1760. It was an imperial octavo, as were the three later editions that were issued in the same year. The book was reprinted again in 1761 and in 1762, evidence that it had a successful sale.

While the Bible was in hand in Cambridge, Baskerville at Easy Hill was working out other ideas. He had long had an ambition to print a series of small books, the classics of Greek and Latin literature, and he had been having the texts prepared and edited. There was also a project to print a Juvenal in quarto. With all these books in hand, Baskerville's press was now gaining an impetus of its own, and the work-rooms must have begun to look a little crowded as formes of type and quires of paper began to accumulate. There is no indication how many men were employed in the business of printing (nor in the japanning side either), but it cannot at any time have been a really large number. There appear to have been at least four presses, two of which were away in Cambridge: each press needed two men, which meant eight men when all the presses were fully manned, a condition which was probably not regular. There must in addition have been three or four compositors, together with a boy or two, and perhaps a couple of labourers. This makes fourteen or fifteen people, a useful number for a small office, and one capable of turning out a lot of work—and of eating up a good deal in the way of wages throughout the year. When the presses lay idle it was an expensive matter. It was no doubt because this establishment had to be kept occupied that Baskerville sought work from the booksellers in London and from private customers, though with little success. It was no doubt also the reason why, later, he began to sell founts of type from his foundry, a thing he had not intended to do, and which it seems he regretted having done; even to the extent of telling the representatives of the prospective buyers of his foundry, later, that he had never sold type. It is probable, however, that as more and more money came to be tied up in the business of printing, and the need to keep the presses going was constantly presented to him, Baskerville began to lower his prices nearer to the common level. He advertised that he was prepared to print at prices little different from those in force among other printers. But it did not serve to get him as many customers as he would have liked.

Such common printing was mere pot-boiling for him, and he seems to have paid little attention to its production. His best work went into his own books, the books he produced at his own venture, to be sold by Dodsley in London. Into these he put all the care and attention to detail he could. As he went through his composing room and his pressroom he must at times have been a great nuisance to his employees, wanting things done in a special way, perhaps against the grain of their experience, or wanting them done again because some small detail did not satisfy him. Paper was printed and then cast aside for such reasons and the work begun anew. In every department he sought perfection and made rules to achieve it, in most things with success, in others with unexpected failure. He wanted his books to be beautiful and inviting to read, and so they were. He wanted them to be accurate, and they were not. Baskerville editions, particularly the classics he was so ambitious to print, are notorious for the number of errors they contain. Yet he paid particular attention to proof-reading. He considered that a man should spell out the copy letter by letter while a proof-reader followed the proof, and that inevitably errors should be discovered in this way. Any proof-reader, I believe, will at once perceive the fallacy of such a method of reading a foreign language, especially, as must be assumed in the case of Baskerville's proof-readers, when they did not understand that language.

In 1761 Baskerville printed an edition of Addison's works for the Tonsons, and another of Congreve's works. He had also progressed with his pocket classics, and Shenstone, writing to a friend, mentions that he has received from

Baskerville a copy of Horace, evidently an advance copy, for the book was not published for some time after. This book had been edited by John Livy, who had now joined Baskerville, or was on call, to serve as editor, and who worked with him on several other volumes.

It had been suggested that the Horace should have illustrations and the delay in publication was due to an expenditure of time in looking for a suitable artist, and in writing backwards and forwards, and in seeing specimens and rejecting them. In the end, the book was not published until the following year, and then with only a frontispiece.

This little book is considered to be among the best works of Baskerville's press.

It was about this time that Baskerville made his one and only excursion into the designing and casting of type faces other than his own characteristic roman. In 1758 he had approached the Oxford University Press with a suggestion that he should cut a new Greek type for them, and they agreed to commission him to do this. He was more than two years in the cutting and casting of the type, and when at last the order was completed and delivered to Oxford, to be used in a book that was waiting for it, it was only to meet with a hostile reception from the learned and unlearned alike. The design, it was said, was poor. The letters were weak and thin, and not all as pleasant as the Greek types that had been in use hitherto. They were strange, too, and like no Greek that man ever saw. These complaints, to modern eyes, do not seem to be justified. The letters of the fount slope, like italics, and they are certainly lighter in general colour than an equivalent roman would be, a common effect of italics, but they are not weak, and they certainly are legible. Baskerville cut no more exotic faces. Henceforth he confined his attention to his roman, and shortly afterwards brought out a specimen sheet showing, for the first time, his type in nonpareil.

The Bible had all this time been proceeding at Cambridge under the watchful eye of Henry Warren, with, no doubt, periodic incursions by Baskerville, by letter and in person. Anxious as he might have been for the perfection of his work, by this time he had begun to tire of the connection with Cambridge, and even to complain of the cost of printing. The money for the Bible had been borrowed, he says in a letter to Horace Walpole, through whom he hoped he might get some official support, and the returns he was getting from the books he had printed for himself and for others were not repaying him for the capital he had engaged. There were, he said, suggestions that he might sell the whole of his enterprise to Russia or to Denmark, where he had sent specimens of his work, but that it was thought that it ought to stay in his own country. Parliament, he had been told, had given a handsome reward for a quack medicine—could it not therefore do something for him. If it could not, he must sacrifice a small patrimony of £74 a year. And so on. A peevish letter, and one that seems to have exaggerated his financial problems. There is no evidence that Baskerville was ever in want. Though it may have been true, and undoubtedly was true, that the business of printing was costing him more than he ever bargained for, it is unlikely that his fortune had been so much diminished that he must sell a patrimony of so little value. Walpole does not appear to have replied to Baskerville's letter.

In England, there was not undisputed fame to balance the financial loss, but abroad Baskerville was better appreciated. The Didots of France and Bodoni in Parma, for example, saw what he was doing and understood the value of it, understood that he was a pioneer and an innovator, and they followed the path on which he had set some of the first signposts.

The publication of the Bible did nothing to improve Baskerville's satisfaction with the business of printing books. Though artistically a great success, which brought new and greater honour to his name throughout Europe, it did not sell in quantities anything like enough to balance the formidable expense of producing it. A large quantity of copies was left on the printer's hands, and remained in his warehouse for years. It represented so much dead money, and Baskerville hated dead money. There was no help for it. Eventually he was reduced to selling the lot to a bookseller for a very low

VI. BASKERVILLE'S HOUSE, EASY HILL, AFTER THE FIRE

VII. BASKERVILLE'S PUNCHES

price—a kind of bargain that is now called remaindering. And yet it is a beautiful book, far better designed and printed than comparable Bibles of the time.

It was a bad time for Baskerville. The year had opened with the death of his stepson John Eaves, after a short illness, and this was a particularly hard blow to the older man who had for so long been as a father to him. This young man, who had come to Easy Hill with his mother twelve or fourteen years before, had so captured the affections of the childless Baskerville that the printer had determined to make him his heir and successor. Baskerville felt the loss so keenly that even four years later he was quoting this bereavement as the reason for wishing to sell his foundry.

Only eleven days later, Shenstone died. Shenstone had been one of Baskerville's firmest friends and keenest admirers —more, he had helped the printer constantly with criticisms, suggestions, and advice. It was Shenstone who had introduced him to Dodsley, who had found this artist and that, as needed, and passed judgement on the work they did, who sent a succession of famous people to visit the printing and japanning workshops, to buy or inscribe their names as subscribers; it was Shenstone, probably, who had found John Livy to act as editor for the classics. The rotund poet in his suit of white silk had been a frequent visitor to Easy Hill, to take tea with Mr. and Mrs. Baskerville, and to discuss the growing of flowers and the planning of gardens, and what book might be printed next, and what were in hand, and what well-known people were come to Birmingham (and they all came to see Shenstone and his gardens, and many to see Baskerville also). Now he too was gone. It was a lonely time for Baskerville.

Many another ageing man—and Baskerville was now approaching sixty—feels the sharp loneliness of the unpeopling stage on which he moves, the empty spaces which can never be filled again. The anodyne was work. Baskerville had always worked, long, laboriously, and methodically, often brilliantly, and he could not stop now, nor wish to. Even Dodsley's death in the next year did not make him pause. Here was another old friend gone, and not only a friend but a close colleague, for Dodsley had all the time remained the publisher of Baskerville's books.

But Baskerville was becoming obsessed with a sense of failure. He measured success by prosperity, and he had had no prosperity in printing. He saw it as a business in which a great deal of his money was locked up, and which ate up more and more money the more he pursued it. He sought yet again to sell his equipment to France, and again he had no success. The price he asked, in the region of eight thousand pounds, was more than the French were willing to pay. Baskerville offered to sell for six thousand pounds, but the response was no different.

Baskerville now adopted a curious course which does not seem to have been properly understood by anyone. He leased his equipment to one of his workmen, Robert Martin, who then 'offered his services at Birmingham to print for Gentlemen or Booksellers on the most moderate terms'. Samples might be seen on sending a line to Robert Martin—or John Baskerville. This 'or John Baskerville' has some significance, for it is clear that it was no mere matter of courtesy on Baskerville's part. He had not retired completely from his press, nor had he left entire control of it to Martin. He was able, as we shall see, to come back into control at will.

Among the first things Martin did was to sell founts of type, so that Baskerville founts were soon to be found in many local printing houses. He then went on to produce a pocket edition in nine volumes of Shakespeare's works, not with any distinction. It is a pity that Baskerville himself did not do this. Martin also produced a slim book called *The Chase*, with fine engravings, and this is a book of real charm, still to be met with in bookshops at no very high price. Baskerville looked on with little interest until Martin began to print sections of an edition of the Bible, as a sub-contractor to a rival printer called Boden. There is no account of how this affected Baskerville, but it may be imagined that he walked one day into the workshop—for men who have been printers can never leave printing entirely alone—and, peering at a galley of newly set type, he found there the familiar words. This was too much. He would not have it. He would not

THE

CONTAINING THE

OLD TESTAMENT

AND

THE NEW:

Tranſlated out of the

AND

With the former TRANSLATIONS

Diligently Compared and Reviſed,

By His MAJESTY's Special Command.

APPOINTED TO BE READ IN CHURCHES.

CAMBRIDGE,

Printed by *JOHN BASKERVILLE,* Printer to the UNIVERSITY.

M DCC LXIII.

CUM PRIVILEGIO.

21. The title-page of the Bible published in 1763.

have a Bible to be produced by an upstart and cheapjack printer like Boden; he certainly would not have part of it printed in his own workshop. He took command again forthwith, and Martin probably left Easy Hill. Baskerville at once set to work to produce another Bible to oust the upstart Boden with a book finer than he might compass, and the presses were engaged upon it. It was announced that the first number, at twopence halfpenny the copy, would be ready on the second of January 1769, and that the whole would be complete in thirty numbers; this, the advertisement stated, was twenty numbers less than Boden's, and thus money was saved. There seems to have been no question or problems of privilege or permission on either side. Boden retaliated with another advertisement, in which he claimed that the number of his issues would be less, not more than Baskerville's, and the difference in prices, not fifteen shillings in favour of Baskerville, but ten shillings in favour of Boden. False, said Baskerville, again in the press, and invited Boden to explain fairly. Boden did, with damaging half compliments to his rival, and more of the complicated arithmetic that made this quarrel possible. Boden, in derision, offered to give any Baskerville subscriber copies of the Boden parts in exchange for the Baskerville ones they had been so misled to buy. Boden decried the quality of Baskerville's paper and his printing, sneered at his inability to persuade the London bookseller's to use his press, and even derided Baskerville's appointment as university printer. Baskerville replied again, in terms no more complimentary. It was not a dignified quarrel, and Baskerville does not come out of it altogether best. It went on for the better part of two years until the Bibles were published complete in 1772. The two editions are so like each other, in illustration and typography, that one must have been copied from the other. Did each printer have a spy in the other's house?

There is no indication of any such difficulties as those Baskerville suffered in getting permission to print his first Bible. If Boden had had to pay for the right to publish the Bible he never said so, which is curious in the circumstances, and there is no evidence that Baskerville had any further dealings with the university about it; indeed, he had ceased to print for the university four years earlier.

During the quarrel Baskerville had issued an edition of Horace in quarto, with illustrations, and had also started to issue those pocket classics that had been his ambition years ago. Between 1770 and 1774 four of these appeared, and there was also an edition of Ariosto's works printed for the Molinis, a firm of booksellers in Paris. Through this firm he tried once again to sell his equipment to France, but the correspondence was once more fruitless.

According to Reed, it is possible that during these years the losses involved in his printing were no longer of moment, and that despite his desire to sell, Baskerville was more contented than he had been. But he was growing old now, and no doubt he would have liked to be clear of this uncertain business, and so be able to leave a good sum to Sarah if he should die first. He had made his will, a document that was to cause a good deal of discussion and scandal when it became known. He expressed his contempt of 'the farce of consecrated ground' and 'the Irish barbarism of sure and certain hopes'; the Revelation he called an impudent abuse of common sense. 'I expect', he said, 'some shrewd remark will be made on this my declaration by the ignorant and bigoted who cannot distinguish between religion and superstition and are taught to believe that morality (by which I understand all the duties a man owes to God and his fellow creatures) is not sufficient to entitle him to divine favour with professing to believe as they call it certain absurd doctrines and mysteries of which they have no more conception or idea of than a horse.' He directed that his body should be buried in his garden in a conical building that he had adapted for the purpose, and which had been used as a mill—possibly a windmill, for he had experimented with windmills during his last months, trying to improve their action, or a mill in which his writing paper was made. Someone had asked him once how he would like to be buried, and he had answered that they could bury him 'sitting, standing, or lying, but that he did not think that they could bury him flying'. He died on the 8th of January 1775. The undertaker,

My further Will & pleasure is and I Hearby Declare that the Devise of Goods & Chattles as above is upon this Express Condition that my Wife in Concert with my Ex.rs to Cause my Body to be Buried in a Conical Building on my own premises Heartofore used as a mill which I have Lately Raised Higher and painted and in a Vault which I have prepared for It. This doubtless to many may appear a Whim perhaps It is So — But is a Whim for many years Resolved upon as I have a Hearty Contempt of all Superstition the Farce of a Consecrated Ground the Irish Barbarism of Sure and Certain Hopes &c. I also Consider Revelation as It is Call'd Exclusive of the Scraps of Morality Casually Intermixt with It to be the most Impudent abuse of Common Sence Which Ever Was Invented to Befool mankind. I Expect Some Serious Remark Will be made on this my Declaration by the Ignorant & Bigotted Who Cannot Distinguish between Religion & Superstition and are Taught to Believe that morality (by which I understand all the Duties a man ows to God and his fellow Creatures) is not Sufficient to Entitle him to Divine favour Without professing to believe as they Call It Certain Absurd Doctrines & mysteries of which they have no more Conception or Idea of than a Horse This morality alone I profess to have been my Religion and the [Rule] of my actions to which I appeal how far my profession and practice have been Consistant Lastly I do Hearby appoint my Worthy Friend M.r Edward Palmer and Josiah Ruston my Wifes Brother Jo.nt Ex.rs of this my Will in that They Will Jointly and Cordially Execute this my most Important Trust Committed to them With Integrity & Candour to Each of Wch I Leave 6 Guineas to Buy a Ring Which I hope they Will Consider as a keepsake In Witness &c—

The Epitaph
Stranger —

Beneath this Cone in unconsecrated Ground
a Friend to the Liberties of mankind Directed his Body to be Inhum'd
    May the Example Contribute to Emancipate thy mind
    From the Idle Fears of Superstition
    And the Wicked arts of Priestwood —

22. The last page of Baskerville's will, written in 1773, with the forthright remarks concerning superstition.

or those instructing him, chose to bury the body standing upright.

Baskerville's house stood upon its hill for only another sixteen years. It was sold to John Rylands in 1789, and in 1791, though defended by its inhabitants, it was sacked and burned by the rioters who stormed about the town in that year. Eight of the rioters, finding the wine cellars, drank themselves silly and were burned to death.

Baskerville's tomb in the garden was not disturbed, however. The body remained inviolate until 1826, when the spread of industry overtook Easy Hill and a canal was constructed through what had once been the garden, and wharves were built. The leaden coffin was uncovered and removed to the warehouse of a man called Gibson, who was at this time the tenant of the Easy Hill property. The coffin was opened, and the body, dressed magnificently in court costume, was found to be in a remarkable state of preservation, despite its forty-six years of burial. Then, even more remarkably, the coffin was closed up again, shoved into an out-of-the-way corner of the warehouse, and promptly forgotten. It seems to have been left there for four or five years, until, when some clearing out of stores was going on, the coffin was rediscovered. Gibson now persuaded a plumber called Marston to take charge of it, and the coffin was therefore removed to Marston's shop. This Marston may have been a descendant of Baskerville's sister, who had married a man of that name, and it was no doubt on the score of kinship that he allowed the burden to be thrust upon him. If so, he was not above making a little money out of his distinguished relative, to pay for his lodging, as it were, and he showed the coffin and its occupant to the public at so much per head.

It seems to have been the intention of Mr. Rylands, the owner of Easy Hill estate, to have the body reinterred, but he was curiously dilatory about getting it done, for the coffin rested in Marston's shop, like an apprentice under the counter, until 1829. Evidently in those days people did not mind the presence of a dead body as much as we do now. There is a parallel in the story of Haydn's body and its

87

severed head, about the same period, showing the same odd toleration of an unburied corpse. Rylands expostulated about the show that was being made of Baskerville's body, but it seems to have been the ordinary, if somewhat delayed, processes of decay, and not decency, that made reburial imperative. Reburial, however, posed a problem that may explain the delay. People believed that Baskerville had been an atheist, though it is doubtful if Baskerville, whose antagonism to religion extended no further than the denial of foolish superstitions, would have recognized himself under such a description. He had certainly attended church in his lifetime, more, had been an officer of the parish—but all that was forgotten now. The local clergy believed him to have been an atheist—and had he not already been buried once in unconsecrated ground? He certainly could not be buried in consecrated ground now. Where then could he be buried? Those who had charge of the body, who were not of the same mind as the living Baskerville, could not conceive that it should be buried anywhere else than in consecrated ground. There then was the problem.

Marston had a vault in St. Philip's church, but the rector would not allow him to bring the coffin into it. A Mr. Knott then offered the use of his vault in Christ Church, if the coffin could somehow be allowed in there. Evidently the rector here was also antagonistic, but there was a plot in hand to circumvent him. Marston consulted one of the churchwardens, a well-known solicitor called Barker. Mr. Barker at once said that he could by no means allow the burial to take place. He kept the keys, he said, and would not hand them over; but he added that at a particular time of day, when he was usually out, they were left upon his hall table. According to the *Birmingham Notes and Queries*, 'Marston was not slow to take the hint, and called (at that time); the door was opened by the butler, and there were the keys. Mr. Marston asked if Mr. Barker was at home; the servant said "no", faced about, and walked off. Mr. Marston took the keys and the reclosed lead coffin was carried "on a handbarrow covered by a green baize cloth" to its last resting place in Mr. Knott's vault in Christ Church.'

But it was not the last resting place, nor the last time Baskerville's remains were to be disturbed. Because of the secrecy of the burial, stories began to circulate about the place of the interment, that, for example, he had been placed beside his wife's body in St. Philip's, despite the parson, that he had been buried in unconsecrated ground again, and so forth. For more than half a century these stories were trafficked about until the truth became uncertain, and just to fix the question, in 1893 the body was exhumed once more. The much enduring Baskerville was still recognizable, or at least he was recognizable to one of the Rylands, who, an octogenarian, had seen the body in his youth, and on this evidence it was decided that the body was truly Baskerville's, despite the fact that the splendid court dress they had expected to see had been replaced by some much dingier and cheaper stuff. Had Marston ended by stripping Baskerville of his gold lace and satin? It looks like it. The coffin was sealed up once more and replaced in the vault.

It was not there for long. The advance of that industry he had done so much to foster overwhelmed Christ Church as it had overwhelmed Easy Hill, and the coffin was brought forth again. It now lies in the Church of England cemetery at Warstone Lane, Birmingham.

After her husband's death in 1775 Mrs. Baskerville sold the stock of books she had on hand and announced that she did not propose to print, but that she would keep the foundry in being for the sale of founts of type. She soon tired of this, and after a fruitless attempt to auction the types, matrices, etc., in 1779, she sold the whole lot to Beaumarchais, the French writer, who had grand ideas for a fine edition of Voltaire, and not only bought the foundry apparatus to that end, but also printing equipment and paper mills, and even a fortress in Kehl to do the printing in. Apart from a few founts in the hands of printers, which could not be expected to endure indefinitely, there remained in England nothing of Baskerville's foundry, after the carts had gone creaking away to the coast, but the Greek type and matrices he had made for the Oxford University Press—which has them still.

However, in March 1953, the French foundry Deberny et Peignot, into whose hands the punches had come, presented them to the Cambridge University Press.

The story of Baskerville's typeface does not end there, nor is it likely to be ended for a long time yet. Though his letter and his style vanished within twenty-five years of his death, and remained forgotten for over a hundred years, when the Monotype Corporation reintroduced the design, as part of the policy of revival of notable type faces that was instituted under the inspiration of Stanley Morison, in 1926, it was soon widely popular. It became plain that the letter had possibilities in the modern world that Baskerville could not have contemplated with equanimity. He thought it impossible for other people to use it to proper effect; and now it is not only the beautiful and delicate letter he thought it to be, needing proper appreciation for its proper use in fine books, but also a strong and sturdy maid of all work which, because of its excellent printing qualities, is as effective in a handbill as it is in a book. There is now a version of Baskerville available on every composing machine, both in England and America, and several typefounders have also produced versions.

If it is not entirely of the kind he sought, Baskerville's fame is permanent.

SENEFELDER
AND THE INVENTION
OF LITHOGRAPHY

As a boy, Alois Senefelder dreamed of being an actor, like his father, Peter, who performed at the Theatre Royal in Munich; but Peter thought that the life of an actor, with its interruptions and uncertainty of employment, was not one that he would like his son to follow. He considered that a more solid and dependable occupation would be better for his son's future, and he therefore sent him to study jurisprudence at Ingolstadt.

A boy's ambitions are not easily demolished by good advice or good intentions, and the influence of the theatre was not so easily eradicated from Alois's mind. While still a student, he performed on several occasions as an actor at private theatres, and he also wrote various dramatic pieces. One of these, *Die Mädchenkenner*, was well received when it was performed, and as a result he sent it to be printed. He made a welcome profit of fifty florins from it.

Soon afterwards, his father died, leaving him without enough money to continue his studies at the university. He had to find some means of making a livelihood, and of course the stage came first to mind. His profit from *Die Mädchenkenner* had greatly impressed him, and he thought that he could make a living by acting and by writing similar pieces. Alas, there is a good deal of difference between the pleasure of an amateur success and the grind of a daily profession, and after two years, Senefelder, finding himself as poor as he had been when he began, and with no promise of success to show for his exertions, decided to leave the profession of the theatre and to become an author.

He was no more successful in this than he had been on the stage. Like many other authors of his age, he had to finance his own publications, to find the printer and to pay him, and the bookbinder also, and his first work left him with a considerable deficit. Yet this unsuccessful venture marked the point at which his fortunes turned towards eventual success.

The arrangements for printing his book had taken him frequently into the printing office, and there he had watched the printers at work. It seemed to him a simple and easy business, and he thought that if he had the type and a small press he could print and publish his own works at much less expense. With that, he might make a success, or at least a living, at authorship. But he had not enough money to buy the materials. If he had had it, he remarks himself, he would have been satisfied, and might never have become the inventor of lithography.

Senefelder was never a man to be put off by lack of money or materials. He would attempt the most extraordinary things and do an immense amount of work to overcome his difficulties. In this case, if he had no type and no press, and no money to buy them, then the only thing to be done was to set about making them for himself. First he thought of engraving letters in steel in order eventually to produce a kind of stereotype, but an essay or two convinced him that he had not the skill for such precise work. He put the idea away for possible use in the future.

Other projects and trials fared no better, either for want of skill or for want of money. It never seems to have occurred to Senefelder, until he tried and had to admit defeat, that he could not hope to succeed immediately in techniques that other men must practise and study for years to achieve competence and dexterity. Nevertheless, Senefelder had assiduity and patience, and he next attempted to emulate the copper engravers by writing with a steel point on a copper plate covered with etching ground. The etching ground was a substance with which he coated the plate, and which protected it from the effect of acid. His steel instrument scratched through the ground, so that when acid was afterwards flowed over the plate it bit through the scratches and eroded troughs or furrows in the shape of the letters he had drawn. The ground was then cleared away, and the plate was covered with ink, and wiped clean again on the surface; but the ink remained in the furrows. Paper pressed down on the plate lifted the ink from the furrows, and came away with the letters printed on its surface. This process entailed writing backwards, and of course, if an appearance of type was to be achieved, it meant very fine and careful lettering.

After some practice, Senefelder felt confident that he had developed a satisfactory method, but he again found himself defeated. Copper plates were expensive, and he could not afford enough of them. The plates he had could be ground down and polished and used again, but this was a very tedious and exhausting business.

It is doubtful whether Senefelder really knew, by this time, why he was looking for a new way of printing; or, rather, for a cheaper and easier way. He had begun by desiring some method of printing his own works, but it seems that that original idea was soon lost or overlaid. He was fully in the grip of a passion that was to hold him all his life—the desire to experiment and to invent, to overcome difficulties by his own ingenuity and wit. And he proved to be an extraordinarily ingenious man.

It was while he was practising his skill on copper plates that it occurred to him that a slab of stone which he had in his workshop might provide a useful surface for writing backwards. This was a piece of Kelheim stone, which is easily polished smooth, and it was this ease of repolishing, compared with the difficulty of polishing copper, which attracted Senefelder's attention.

That glance at the stone, the idea of using it, were important. The prefix 'litho' in lithography means 'stone', and Senefelder, however tentatively, had now come to the basis of the invention for which he was to become famous.

Lithographic stones are used to this day as convenient

surfaces on which to mix the thick, paste-like inks that printers use on the press; and it was for this very purpose that Senefelder had bought his stone. Fortunately he had not used it yet. Since he had bought the stone for this express purpose, it is possible that it was common practice in printing houses in that part of Germany, and that lithographic stones found their place in printing long before they found their place on the press. The stone is a variety of limestone found in the Bavarian hills, and particularly good at Sölnhofen. It occurs naturally in flat slabs, and is remarkable for the smooth and silky surface that can be obtained by grinding and polishing.

Senefelder did not think of the stone as other than a more convenient surface on which to practise his process of lettering. He found that it was more comfortable and sympathetic to his hand than copper, and that it was easier to do good work on it; while the facility with which he could erase the writing and repolish the surface was very convenient. Later, it occurred to him that the stone might be used as a printing surface in place of copper, and he set about finding how it could be done.

In his various trials of writing on the stone, he had mixed up a special ink of wax, soap, and lampblack, which took well on it and a curious and famous accident now occurred which was to settle the direction of his experiments, and from which, indeed, a great printing industry was to spring even in his own lifetime.

Senefelder lived in his mother's house, where he had a small workshop or laboratory—the words meant the same thing in his day. Here he was working when his mother interrupted him. The laundrywoman was at the door, and there was no paper in the house on which Frau Senefelder might make a record of the things she was sending to be washed. Could Alois supply a sheet of paper? Alois could not. There was no notepaper in the house because, no doubt, Alois had abstracted it all and used it for his printing experiments. There was none in the workshop for the same reason. At a loss what to do, while the laundrywoman waited impatiently, Senefelder looked about him, and his eye fell upon the Kelheim stone newly polished, and his ink conveniently near it. He seized a pen and rapidly scribbled down the list of articles his mother was sending, and off she went, satisfied to have her record, but surely not without complaint for the vanished notepaper.

Later, when the list was no longer needed, Senefelder was about to erase it, when it occurred to him to try to etch the surface of the stone as it was. He reasoned that the acid would have no effect on the writing, because the ink would resist erosion, while elsewhere the surface would be eaten away. The writing should then be left in relief.

He pursued this idea at once by building a wall of wax round the edge of the stone, to hold the acid on the surface; then he poured over it a mixture of nitric acid and water. The acid ate away the surface as he expected, and he obtained a very shallow relief—the letters stood above the background by the thickness of a piece of stout paper or card. This was too shallow for ordinary inking methods, but he found that he could ink it successfully with cloth wrapped round a piece of board, and he was able to get good impressions.

He considered this a worthwhile invention, which ought to be patented, and all that remained was to make a commercial proposition of it. Once again he was defeated by lack of capital, which prevented him from equipping himself as he thought necessary. Riches, it seemed, lay just beyond his reach, and only beyond his reach because of present lack of money. He determined on a desperate expedient. At that time a man who was called for service in the army could send a substitute, and a substitute could be found—for a fee. Senefelder offered himself as a substitute in the artillery for a friend, who promised to pay him two hundred florins. Senefelder's rather wild idea was to spend all his leisure time in operating his new invention, and he hoped that the proceeds would be enough for him to buy himself out of the army.

In this frame of mind he went off to Ingoldstadt to join his regiment. His first night in barracks dismayed him because of the filthy condition of the place and the crude jests of the soldiers—clearly he would have made a very unhappy soldier. Fortunately for him, at his examination next day, the fact came out that he had been born in Prague (when his father was acting there), and it was decided that technically he could not be regarded as a native of Bavaria; he was therefore ineligible for service in the army.

Dejectedly, Senefelder returned home. He must now seek out some other way of making money. He decided to abandon what remained of the shadowy idea of becoming an author, which had first led him into experiments with etching and Kelheim stones, and to become solely and simply a jobbing printer, undertaking any orders he could get. The sight of some badly printed music in a shop window gave him the notion that he could do a great deal better than that, and he went to see a friend called Gleissner, who was a musician in the Elector's band.

Gleissner, as luck would have it, was about to publish some pieces of sacred music, and the eager inventor showed him various samples of his new process, and promised him satisfaction. The musician was pleased with what he saw, and he and Senefelder came to an agreement for the production of the work.

Senefelder's equipment now included an old engraving press, which he had recently bought, and with this he was able to print the stones for Gleissner's music very well. The project was a complete success, and in the end he found himself with a profit of seventy florins. Once again he saw riches for himself in the future.

Some other orders he got through the good offices of Gleissner yielded a profit, which they shared between them, and it now seemed proper to Senefelder to lay the details of his process before the Electoral Academy of Sciences. He hoped to see his invention mentioned honourably in the transactions of the society, especially since the process of printing was so economical—why, he told them, even the press cost only six florins. The result of this candour was quite different from anything he had expected. The vice-president of the society sent him a present of twelve guineas, with the hope that double the expenses of his press would compensate him for his trouble. No mention in the trans-

VIII. ALOIS SENEFELDER

IX. OTTMAR MERGENTHALER

actions, no encomiums, no encouragement, nor any recognition that he had done anything remarkable.

There was nothing to be done but to carry on as a printer. Senefelder and Gleissner continued to work together, and soon they began to prosper. The old press began to prove too slow and unproductive, and Senefelder designed a new one to print more quickly and more efficiently. Unwittingly, he altered the principle in some minor detail, and this was sufficient to make the new press a complete failure. He could not discover what the fault was, and in the meantime he was producing unsatisfactory work and wasting quantities of paper. In desperation he constructed other presses, with no better results. One of these presses depended for its operation on a large stone of three hundred pounds in weight, which it was liable to fling violently into the air. A narrow escape from destruction by this cannon ball led him at last to abandon this malevolent machine.

Senefelder constructed various other presses, learning from each one more of the fundamental requirements of a good printing press. He was assisted in printing with them by Gleissner and his wife, and while the printing was done by the three of them it was generally good; but when Mrs. Gleissner could not come and Senefelder employed soldiers as workmen instead, the result was poor work and much spoiled paper, and sometimes a good customer lost to the engravers of music.

Although he was now printing entirely from stones by the process I have described, and his process could reasonably be called lithography because of this, his printing surface was in relief and a modern printer would call it rather an adaptation of the letterpress principle. The development of this relief 'lithography' into the planographic variety to which we now give the name did not come until 1798. Once again, the result was an accident, a side product of an experiment aimed at something quite different.

Senefelder had been trying to find a satisfactory method of transferring a written image on to the stone. Lettering drawn directly on to the stone had necessarily to be drawn reversed left to right, and when there was a great deal to

23. Senefelder's first successful lithographic press. The stone is seen on the horizontal platform. Suspended above it is an upright with a scraper on the end: pressure on the footboard at the bottom brings the scraper down to apply pressure on the paper laid on the inked stone.

do this reverse working was always irksome. He sought a method which would allow the writing to be done on paper the right way round, and then transferred to the stone, either as a guide for writing or lettering there, or preferably as a final image.

The ink he had invented earlier was a greasy ink, and during his experiments with transferring, at one stage he used gum dissolved in water with aqua fortis (nitric acid). He noticed that wherever the stone was dampened with this solution, the greasy ink could not be made to adhere. He drew lines on the stone with soap, wetted the surface with

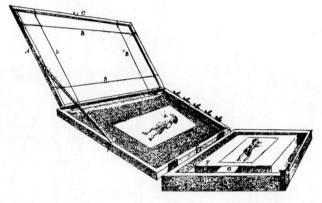

24. A lithographic stone with an image on it, fixed in the printing frame seen in position on the press in figure 23. The paper is placed on the leather stretched on the middle frame, the tympan, and is held there by the frisket, which folds down over it. Both together then fold down on the stone. The scraper applies pressure through the leather.

the gum solution, and then applied the ink. It took only on the soap lines.

The next stage was to apply some definite image to the stone. He found that his pen and ink did not give the clear sharp lines he had hoped for. He discovered that he could get what he wanted only from a stone that had been washed all over first with soapy water or linseed oil; in this condition the stone gave all the quality he desired. Such a stone, however, would have taken the ink all over and would therefore print solid black. It was necessary to remove the soapy water or linseed oil without damaging the image. Washing with nitric acid was the answer to this problem. The stone was

25. A more advanced press designed by Senefelder. The stone is visible, with the leather tympan and the frisket to the right of it and the scraper ready to be hinged down and fixed to the stirrup. Pressure is applied by means of the footboard, and the stone assembly is drawn under the scraper by turning the handles attached to the axle of the pulley.

washed with this, and afterwards it was washed over again, this time with gum water, which could not wet the greasy image.

The stone now had two distinct chemical qualities. First,

there was the ground, or non-printing area, washed with gum, which had an affinity for water, but which had no affinity for grease; and second, there was the image, drawn in greasy ink and therefore with an affinity for grease, but with no affinity for water. Senefelder at last had in his possession the full secret of lithographic printing in the proper sense of the word. No relief of any kind was necessary. The surface was quite flat, and the image on it, whatever it might be, was distinguished only in that it was drawn in a greasy or waxy medium, while the areas that were to remain

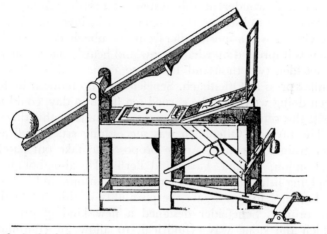

26. A third Senefelder press, with a counterweight to lift the scraper after each impression.

white on the paper were dampened with water on the stone. The repulsion of grease and water is so positive that the finest lines and the heaviest solids remain intact, and neither grease nor water can spread into the other's territory. A greasy ink applied to a surface so differentiated will adhere only to the image, and it will be rejected completely by the damped areas.

An image which could be inked in this manner could obviously be printed by pressing paper into contact with it, and Senefelder already had presses with which this could be done. With a new lever press which he had designed his output could be considerably increased. He now needed more help than he had had, and he brought his two brothers Theobald and George into his employment and also engaged two apprentices. The business had plenty of work to do, and now Senefelder and Gleissner looked forward hopefully to prosperity. A privilege, or patent right, for fifteen years was obtained in Bavaria.

The protection of this privilege, though its force extended no farther than the boundaries of Bavaria, seems to have made Senefelder feel so secure that he was willing to explain the secrets of his process to anyone, and many people came to see and wonder at this system of printing from a flat surface, and to listen to the discourse of its inventor. Among the visitors was a music seller from Offenbach, called Andre. He was impressed by what he saw and heard, and he offered Senefelder two thousand florins to come and establish a similar press in Offenbach. Senefelder, who thought he had been doing well when he earned ten florins a day, could not resist this offer, and an agreement was made forthwith.

The press in Offenbach was successfully established and men trained to run it. Andre proposed to take out patents in London, Vienna, Paris, and Berlin. He also thought of applying lithography to the printing of cottons, and he went to England to investigate the possibility of this. To further the project, Senefelder designed a new kind of press, in which the stone was cylindrical, to allow for continuous printing, but Andre found that cylinder printing of materials was already well known in England, and he did not pursue further the application of lithography to it. However, he sent Senefelder to London afterwards, with one of his brothers, so that he could see what there was to be seen, and so that he could be on hand during the negotiation of the patent.

This visit, which ought to have been valuable experience for a person as observant as Senefelder, proved to be a misery and an annoyance. Andre's brother Philip feared that the secret might get out before the protection of the patent was achieved, and he was determined not to take risks. He compelled Senefelder to live in comparative seclusion and prevented him from moving about. Senefelder's apparent willingness to tell everything to anyone suggests that Philip's precautions were not unnecessary.

During the following years, Senefelder travelled extensively in Germany and Austria, supported by one patron or another, experimenting, building machines, instructing partners in the mystery of lithography, losing all his money in an ill-fated partnership in Austria, recovering, but never making his fortune. He gave a great deal of his time to experiment and produced a number of ideas that are valuable in lithography even today. For example, he worked out the method of transferring by which a drawing made by an artist on paper might be transferred to a litho stone without further intervention of the artist, so that it could then be printed. No problem seems to have daunted him. A difficulty had only to be stated, and he was off in quest of a solution for it.

He realized that the stones used in his presses were very heavy and inconvenient to handle, and he set himself to find a more portable substitute. He invented a material which could be spread on paper or cloth to form a surface like stone, and which could then be drawn on like stone, and printed from in the same way. He also experimented with metals, and found that these, suitably treated, could also be used as printing surfaces for the lithographic press, a discovery which foreshadowed a development of lithography which was not to come for a century or more.

As lithography spread and all sorts of people began to practise it, Senefelder was concerned to find that some printers considered it troublesome and uncertain. He decided, rightly, that the trouble lay rather in the inefficiency of the operator than in the method. He therefore designed a new press which automatically inked and damped the plate, and which made up in some degree for the faults of human error.

He had often been pressed to write his own account of the history and technique of lithography and this at last he did. The book was translated and was published in English in 1819. It is a remarkable book, lucid and very well written, and so thorough in technique that it remained valid as a textbook for decades after his death. He gives a detailed account of his inventions, and mentions various other inventions also, some that are astonishing even today.

He lived to see lithography grow to be a distinct industry, flourishing in England, France, and Germany, and in other countries, and he was honoured by the King of Saxony, the Tsar of Russia, and the king of his own native Bavaria. He died in 1834 at the age of sixty-two.

In a hundred and sixty years the art of lithography, as Senefelder called it, has changed considerably, but in no way beyond what Senefelder would have understood. Thin metal plates have replaced the ponderous stones almost completely, and the method of printing direct from the plate or stone on to the paper has become obsolete. In modern presses the thin, flexible printing plate, bearing the image, is wrapped round a cylinder, where it is automatically damped and inked. It prints only on to another cylinder in contact with it. This second cylinder is covered by a rubber blanket, which receives the image; and this cylinder revolves against a third cylinder, with the paper passing between them and taking the image from the rubber blanket. This is called offset printing, because the image from the printing cylinder is offset on to the rubber-covered cylinder, and from that on to the paper. Modern offset presses produce very fine work at high speeds—up to seven or eight thousand sheets per hour.

The idea of using a thin flexible plate was Senefelder's— had he not worked out a material for applying to paper and cloth for this purpose, and even experimented with metals? He does not, however, seem to have thought of the idea of offsetting the image in the modern manner, as he might easily have done—for this would have solved many of his difficulties by allowing him to do his lettering the right way round.

Today offset lithography is extensively used, and is rapidly increasing in use not only in the factory but in offices, where small machines turn out forms and leaflets rapidly. It is also used for printing boards and for printing tin with the patterns to be seen in any grocer's shop.

The image on the plate is now in most cases put there by photography, and photographs as well as type and drawings can be printed, in as many colours as are required. It seems to be the process that is most conveniently allied to new developments in photographic type composition now under way.

THE PRINTING MACHINE
AND FREDERICK KOENIG

I. THE HAND-PRESS

IT should not be thought that a press—a machine for applying pressure—was something unknown before the invention of printing. Many crafts and industries had long before felt the need for some means of obtaining pressure readily, and presses of various kinds had been developed for special purposes. The wine-grower, for example, had a press to squeeze the juice from the grapes, the cheese-maker had a press with which to compact his product; and the bookbinder also had a press, with which he formed his book. There were others also. All of them worked on the same basic principles, deriving their power from the thrust of a large wooden screw, which was usually turned by levers pushed into holes in its side, like turning a capstan.

When printing was invented, this principle was familiar, and probably the inventor would not at first, in pursuing his experiments, need to do more than to adapt one of these presses to his own special purposes.

The bookbinder's arming press would prove very suitable, and it is possible that for a man interested in the manufacture of books it was also the most familiar. This is a vertical press with the screw ending in a flat plate, below which is another flat plate. Turning the screw brings the two plates together and considerable pressure can be applied to anything between them. This kind of press would serve at first, though it would not be convenient, and it would be very slow to operate. The forme of type would be placed on the lower surface, where it would be inked and the paper would be laid on it, with on top of that a few waste sheets to soften the pressure. The screw would then be turned until the upper plate came down firmly to press the paper on to the type. For work of this kind the opening of the press must be large, and a good deal of screw-turning would have to be done to close the press and to open it again for every single

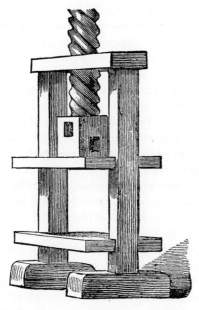

27. A bookbinder's press that might be adapted for a printing
press of an elementary kind.

sheet printed. There could not possibly be any great speed, and there could be no control of register, and very little of quality. Still, it would serve for experiment, and it would show that printing was possible.

The first and most obvious improvement that was needed was some means by which the forme might be inserted and withdrawn for inking and the travel of the screw be reduced to obviate the constant turning. This could be done by making the lower surface of the press, which has come to be known as the bed or coffin, large enough to extend beyond the upper pressure plate, which is known to the printer as the platen. On the extension the forme could be laid, and inked with leather balls filled with sand and wool or horsehair—at least, these were used later for the purpose, and probably also in the early days. A sheet of dampened paper would be laid on the forme, the packing would be placed over it, and the whole lot could then be slid along the bed until it came under the raised platen. This arrangement meant that the throat or opening of the press need not be much more than the height of the type, and therefore one pull of the lever would be enough to bring the platen down on the forme. It was a dead pull, demanding considerable strength of the pressman, and ancient wood-cuts of printing houses generally show pressmen as well-muscled individuals. Beneath the press there might be a block fixed to the floor, on which the man could push with his foot and so gain purchase for the pull, and the press itself was massively built and fixed both to the floor and the roof to counter the pressure.

With all this there was not enough power in the early press to print more than a comparatively small forme. One page seems to have been as much as they could manage, to judge from wood-cuts. It is always surprising how much pressure is needed to get a good impression from a forme of type. Now any book which is sewn at the spine, as books then and since have been, must be made up of sheets of not less than four pages of type—four pages, two leaves, in effect, one sheet folded down the middle; such sheets can be inserted one into the other to form sections of eight, twelve, or sixteen pages, which can then be sewn through the fold, and so on to the next section. For a section of four pages, the pressman at the hand-press had to send the sheet through the press four times, to print two pages on one side and two pages on the reverse.

While the pressman was busy pulling the lever, his assistant was applying more ink to the ink balls—they were always used in pairs—and he would do a sort of dervish dance, banging and rubbing the two balls together to distribute the ink as evenly as possible over their surfaces.

28. An early printing press, from a wood-cut dated 1507. In the background is a compositor with his copy on a stick and his type case before him. The pressman's assistant manipulates a pair of ink balls. The press is braced to the ceiling, but it is light in construction. Other illustrations show presses of much heavier build.

After each bout on the press, the printed sheet was removed and hung over a line for the ink to dry.

If thirty sheets were printed within the hour by this ponderous process, it must have been considered very satisfactory; and of course it was wonderful, phenomenal, in an age which was used to copying books by writing.

The history of the infancy of the printing press is derived principally from the wood-cut illustrations that many early printers used for their signs or trade-marks. The earliest of

29. An example of the heavier kind of hand-press, built with great strength, and firmly braced to the ceiling.

these shows a machine which, while still primitive, is more advanced than the hypothetical press I have been describing. The improvements were important, and made not only for more rapid working, but also for better printing. The bed was made movable, so that by turning a handle connected with a system of straps, the entire bed, with the forme on it, could be moved under the platen and out again. Another improvement was the provision of a pair of frames hinged to the outer end of the bed. The lower frame, or tympan, was covered with stretched parchment or vellum; on this pins or gauges were fixed, and the paper was laid to these, on the vellum, instead of being put on the type. The upper frame was hinged to the top of the lower frame; this was the

30. A ponderous press, free from attachment to the ceiling, but evidently meant for heavy work.

frisket. It was open, with cross strings or covered with paper in which holes were cut. When the paper to be printed was placed on the tympan, the frisket was folded down over it and the string or paper held the sheet in position. The two frames together then folded down on the type, the handle was turned, and the whole lot moved under the platen.

This arrangement meant that the paper could be more securely controlled, smudges were less likely to occur, and some sort of register of one colour on another was possible.

It also meant an increase in speed of operation, for while the pressman was removing the sheet from the tympan and placing the new one his assistant could be inking the type.

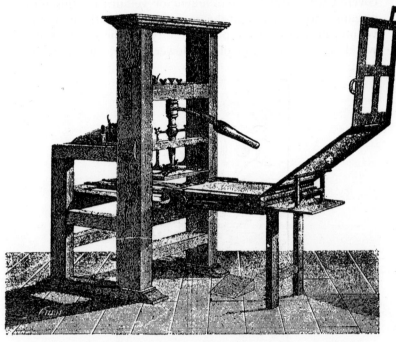

31. An eighteenth-century wooden hand-press. The tympan and the frisket are raised and the bed is open to receive the forme. Beneath the press is a block for the pressman's foot. Detail apart, there is little in this press that cannot be traced in the press of 1507 in figure 28.

Early in the sixteenth century the hand press had arrived at a principle which remained unchanged until the end of the eighteenth century. Although there were certainly advances in the manufacture of hand presses, and they came to be made less ponderously and with more grace, fundamentally they were little different in 1780 than they were in 1500. Their limited production, and limited quality of work, satisfied the world for three hundred years. Any large printing house might have fifty or sixty of these presses, and sometimes they were organized in gangs or groups for greater production. Firms of this size, however, were not common, and the typical printer of the day of the wooden hand-press is rather the man with three or four presses only, while many printers must have made do with only one.

There was no great demand for print as we understand it. There were few people who could read, or were used to reading, and consequently there were few books, and few or no newspapers. It was not until the eighteenth century that literacy began to spread, aided by and itself supporting the rise of the romantic novel and the appearance of various news sheets. It was not until then, with increased need as the goad, and the new science of mechanics as an inspiration, that the printing machine began to enter the phase of rapid development that has brought it to the high state of efficiency of today.

At a time when iron-foundries throughout the country were waking up to the astonishing things that can be done with iron, from the building of bridges to the construction of steam engines, it was inevitable that sooner or later someone

32. The Stanhope, the first iron press, with a new system of leverage to provide a better and easier impression.

must try to build a printing press of iron. John Baskerville had introduced metal into his press in the middle of
the century, but that was merely for a part of it; for the
main construction he was content with wood. The first all-

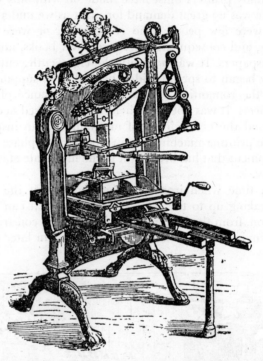

33. The Columbian hand-press. Despite its irrelevant ornament,
this was an efficient machine, and it was popular in America and
in England. The eagle is not only a patriotic decoration, but also
a counterweight to raise the platen, to which it can be seen to be
linked. The impression lever no longer operates a screw, but a
system of toggle joints, which give greater pressure.

metal press was designed some thirty years later by Earl
Stanhope. It was a heavy and ponderous thing, but it was
practical and efficient, and because of a system of levers
controlling the impression, it needed much less effort to
operate. It marked the end of the wooden hand-press.

In Stanhope's press, the wooden screw was replaced by

the levers, which considerably increased the pressure, and so allowed a larger forme to be printed.

The Stanhope was followed by other hand-presses made of iron, many of which came and passed and have been forgotten, but two of the newcomers, the Columbian from the

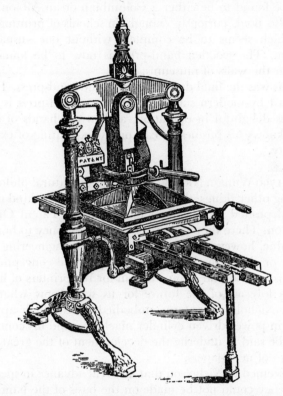

34. The handsome and efficient Albion, as simple and classical in design as the Columbian is gothic and florid.

U.S. and the Albion from England, achieved greater and more permanent popularity. By means of toggle joints these presses made yet better use of the force applied. They could be operated by anyone of normal strength, and their output was good, with excellent quality in the hands of a good man.

The Stanhope is very rare in England these days, though still to be found on the Continent, in use as a proofing press, or in the hands of an amateur, or worse, in the workshop of an arty-crafty enthusiast printing limited editions, which are supposed, *ipso facto*, to be superior to books printed on a powered machine. In England, where a hand-press is in use for any of these purposes, and there are plenty of them, it will be found to be either a Columbian or an Albion. They are also used, curiously enough, in schools of printing, none of which seems to be complete without one—usually an Albion. The wooden hand-press is now to be found only within the walls of museums.

This was the final development of the hand-press. Though not fast by modern standards, the iron hand-press is nevertheless delightful in operation, and in the hands of a man who knows his business it can produce printing of excellent quality.

In 1790 William Nicholson, a writer on natural philosophy, among other things, designed a completely new kind of press and deposited specifications of it with the Patent Office in London. There they still are. He had no money to build this machine, however, and probably not the engineering knowledge or skill either. Merely on paper, the conception was astonishing, a kind of pipe dream for the printers of his day, but a forecast of the future for us who know what came after. Nicholson's patents embodied ideas which appeared later in power-driven cylinder machines, and his conception may be said to underlie the development of the great rotary presses of newspapers.

It seemed to Nicholson that any real advance in speed and efficiency could not be made on the basis of the hand-press, whether of wood or iron; speed only came with rotary motion. The in-and-out movement of the coffin and the up-and-down movement of the platen of the hand-press imposed limitations from which there was no escape in any conventional direction. Nicholson saw that cylinders revolving one against the other suffered from no such restriction. There was nothing highly original in that observation, but there certainly was in the machine that he conceived on the basis of this rotary motion. The type was to be set and attached by some means to the surface of a cylinder, and a second cylinder was to revolve in contact with the first, so that a sheet of paper fed between the two would be pressed in contact with the type and printed. It obviously would not do to attempt to ink the type on such a cylinder with ink balls; nothing less than automatic inking would do, and Nicholson provided for this by means of a system of rollers which would distribute the ink evenly before applying it to the type. He gave detailed instructions for covering the rollers with layers of woollen cloth and leather. This inking system was in itself a revolutionary idea. If he had put his machine into practice, Nicholson would no doubt have found, as did others who attempted the same thing, that rollers of leather are not satisfactory; they will give inking of a kind, but not of a good kind. The solution of this particular problem did not arise until many years later, when a printer, visiting a pottery, noticed that a rubbery kind of material was used for stamping patterns on to pots. Finding that it was made simply of glue and treacle melted together, he resolved to try it as a covering for the ink balls in his press-room. It proved excellent. It was not immediately considered as a covering for rollers, but it was not long before Bryan Donkin, a printing engineer, found a method of casting a cylinder of the material on a metal stock and the most serious problems of inking were solved.

Nicholson's ideas have come in for a great deal of adverse comment from people who affirm that it is not difficult to imagine a machine, but that it is quite a different matter to put it into practice and to make it work. It is true that there seem to be obvious faults in the description of the machine contained in the patent, and ideas that are improbable—the fixing of the type on the cylinder, for example, is one that is not satisfactorily resolved. Certainly it is easy to conceive a wonderful new machine; most of us can do it, and probably have done it. It is quite a different matter, in one age, to design a machine that adumbrates the development of machines of that kind for a hundred years after one's death. No one ever yet designed a new invention which was exactly right as it was set down on paper; there are always things to be tested, to be developed, to be altered. If Nicholson had been a more persistent character, and if he had had an Andre Bauer and a Thomas Bensley, then it is possible that the invention of the printing machine might have been attributed to him. But none of these circumstances prevailed, and he therefore remains a seer, a clairvoyant who saw the direction of progress, but did not in fact succeed in any practical measure in advancing it.

2. FREDERICK KOENIG

A hand-press is a machine, a printing machine. There can be no doubt of that. Since the hand-press had been in operation for centuries before he was born, we should know what we mean when we call Frederick Koenig the inventor of the printing machine, for the description is apt enough, and correct. The hand-press was a dead end, a development that, despite its long reign, led to nothing. From the machine invented by Koenig has come all the long line and wide variety of the modern printing press.

What Koenig set out to invent, and what he did in the end invent, was a power-driven press that would work faster and with less attendance than the wooden hand-press with which he became familiar when he served his apprenticeship in the printing house of Breitkopf & Haertel at Leipzig.

Koenig's first efforts were directed towards the production of a machine which was simply the conventional hand-press adapted for a power drive, and it had just about as much driving machinery as there was press.

The human mind comes upon new ideas reluctantly and laboriously, and invariably attempts to interpret them or to implement them in terms of pre-existent conceptions. It was as inevitable, no doubt, that the first power printing press should look like a hand-press as it was that the first motorcar should look like a horseless carriage. It was inevitable just because the hand-press was the only kind of printing machine that Koenig knew, or that anyone knew. In the press-room of Breitkopf & Haertel there were a number of them, of all sorts, and Koenig no doubt studied them with

care, for at an early age he decided that he meant to invent
a printing machine.

He was enrolled as an apprentice compositor and printer
at the age of fifteen in 1789, and the intention seems to have
been that he should learn all sides of the business of printing.
His indenture was to run from the feast of Saint John in 1790
—the difference in dates suggests a period of probation—to
the same feast in 1795. For some reason that is not clear he
was liberated on Saint Michael's day in 1794.

In the meantime his father had died in 1791, leaving his
mother with little money, and Koenig with a desire to
provide for her which was to worry him for many years after,
to worry him because he had on many occasions to write to
her to say that he could not send her any money; and sometimes to say that, though he had no money, things were
going to be better and that he would soon be well off.
Sometimes he could not write to her at all, or he wrote without knowing whether his letters would ever be delivered; for
the French revolutionary wars were soon to come, and
during the years that Koenig spent in England communica-
tion with the Continent, upset by continual strife, became
difficult and tortuous.

After the end of his apprenticeship Koenig seems to have
joined the university of Leipzig, not as a registered student,
but as some sort of supernumerary, to listen to lectures on
science. For now, as he says, he determined to abandon the
trade of printing and to devote himself to scientific matters.
He seems to have studied anthropology and philosophy,
modern languages and history. None of these subjects
indicated his future interest in machinery. He may have
worked as a printer during the day in order to support himself as a student in what spare time he could manage, and
perhaps he also put to use his learning in languages by
working as a translator for the booksellers. Certainly he
wandered about the country, for he was also in Hamburg
and in Greifswald, where he worked for a time in a library
run by an uncle.

It must have been at Greifswald that he learned the library
business sufficiently to enter into an agreement with one

Riedel and his wife. Riedel was a man of some wealth, and is described by some writers as a miser. He agreed with Koenig to provide the sum of five thousand thalers for the foundation of a library which Koenig was to manage. Koenig undertook on his side to use the five thousand thalers faithfully, conscientiously, and to the best advantage in the library venture; but there was also a clause in the contract that part of the money might be used to establish a printing house annexed to the library. There were very few conditions. Like the people who lent Gutenberg money, the Riedels were surprisingly trusting and complaisant; and like Gutenberg, Koenig turned out in the end to be a poor investment. When a man is led away by a grand idea, which he sees within the bounds of his abilities, money, and the people who own it, have not the importance they have to more ordinary people. Let them wait, let them wait! When the ship comes home—and of course it *must* come home, there is no doubt of that—they will be paid. But the ship is generally such a slow mover, such a long time in getting into harbour. The Riedels got their money in the end, after many fretful and anxious letters following many long silences. Koenig seems to have regarded their plaints with irritation, as impositions on his time from impossible or importunate people, but there is every reason to sympathize with them and to understand why they should be concerned about the large sum they had lent to the bustling young man who promised so much. It was many years before they were paid, and a war and a world away from the lending of the money.

It was about the time of the agreement with Riedel, about the year 1802, that Koenig seems to have first begun to think seriously about the construction of a printing machine. He thought about it so much that the foundation of the library, for which he had borrowed the money, was forgotten, and some, or all of the money was used in experiments and the construction of the machine that filled his thoughts. Riedel seems to have agreed to this course, his mind changed, no doubt, by the eagerness, the faith, and the persistence of the young Saxon; but Riedel could not have dreamed that twelve years later he would still be asking for his money, and that Koenig would be reminding him tartly that he had agreed to its use for the invention of a printing machine, as though the necessity for such a reminder ought never to have arisen. There had been an intention, after the idea of the library, that a printing business should be purchased, and Koenig went to Mainz to see about one. He seems to have bought one too, though little more than that is known, except that at the same time he had some typographical property in Suhl or at Meiningen.

What happened to the printing house at Mainz? It was apparently sold very soon after it was acquired, for Koenig now needed, not a printing house, which could occupy only his time and tie up the capital he had borrowed, but the capital itself, with which to further his project for a machine. He set up a workshop in Suhl and there started to build his new press. Suhl was a town noted for the manufacture of armaments, and perhaps Koenig came there because in such a place he was more likely to find the men and the workshops to make the specialized parts he would need.

His first idea was to mechanize the hand-press as he knew it, and it seems probable that he simply took an ordinary hand-press and adapted it to suit his purpose. It differed from the simple hand-press in various details. He designed an inking system, for example, which would do away with the labour of the pressman's assistant. As he conceived it, his press would have saved labour, but it seems doubtful whether it would have saved any time. He began to think of some means by which the reciprocal motions of the press might be linked with the rotary movement of an engine, a steam engine preferably, or perhaps a water engine. However, before he could go any further, he must get more money and he therefore looked about him for support. He was not long in finding printers who agreed to give him commissions for machines, and on this basis he went ahead.

He was not at this time so immersed in his plans and projects as to have no time for social intercourse. He made many friends in Suhl, and among them was a girl called Johanna Hoffmann, the daughter of an official of the town, a pompous and ambitious gentleman with decided ideas

about his own station. The friendship between Koenig and
Johanna deepened, the two fell in love, and proposed to
marry. This idea was entirely abhorrent to the girl's father.
He thought that a man like Koenig, a dabbler with no
income and no prospects, was a poor thing for a son-in-law.
He told his daughter so, repeatedly, until the poor girl's
home became uncomfortable for her. Koenig was distressed,
and this, joined to some difference he had with the landlord
of his workshop, led him to quit Suhl and to move to Meiningen. Here he became interested in the possibilities of stereotyping, as a result of reading of the experiments of Lord
Stanhope. Koenig always kept his ears open and was ready
to pounce on anything that might lead him to something
new. Johanna faded out of his life.

The unfortunate girl remained with her father, who never
ceased to deny the worth of the foot-loose young inventor,
while he praised the merits of a rival whose circumstances
conformed more with the father's ambitions. Johanna was
prevailed upon at last, and no doubt despairing of Koenig,
she married her father's choice. She was to meet Koenig
again many years later.

Before he left Suhl, Koenig had succeeded in producing a
printing machine. It was simply a mechanized hand-press,
built of wood, but it did what it was intended to do. If this
was no great matter, no more than the saving of some
amount of wages, at least it was something done, and Koenig
had proved to himself that he could make a printing
machine and that he could make it work. Putting it on the
market was a different matter. He needed money to finance
him, capital with which to build the machines until they
were ready for sale, and he now sought for some source of
supply. Here he met with such a poor reception that he was
cast into despair. His machine seemed to arouse little interest
among printers, and he found himself unable to communicate
his enthusiasm for progress to the hard-headed business men
who ran the larger printing houses about him. Nor could he
find anyone to show interest in his new method of stereotyping, which in some manner involved the use of stone, not
metal. It must be understood, Koenig remarked, that this

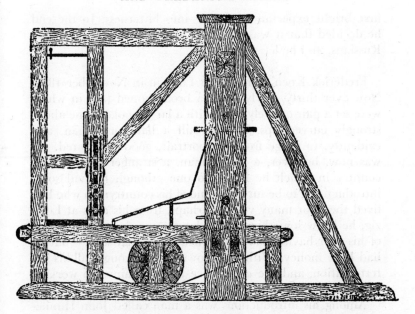

35. Koenig's wooden printing machine, a mechanized hand-press, made at Suhl. The inking system is shown in black on the second upright from the left, with the forme as a heavy black line, and the tympan and frisket inclined against the main upright. Rotation of the pulley moved the forme from left to right, under the inking roller to the platen, behind the main upright.

method was not to be confused with that used by Andre at Offenbach—which was, in fact, the lithography of Sene-felder. Nothing more seems to be known of this interesting project.

Among the many people in high places that Koenig addressed in search of capital was the Tsar of Russia. From the court of that august gentleman came a reply that seemed to promise some possibility of progress, and Koenig under-took the long journey to St. Petersburg, in high hope. He found himself at once enmeshed in the bureaucracy that governed all the actions of the Russian court, the promise still held out, but fulfilment prevented by constant delays, procrastinations, stupidities, and all kinds of difficulties. Koenig remained in St. Petersburg until the autumn, his first bright expectations fading into bitterness. In the end he decided that it was useless to expect anything from the Russians, and he left for London.

Frederick Koenig arrived in London in November 1806. Now over thirty, burly, with a broad-boned face in which were set a pair of lively eyes, with a large hooked nose above strongly curved lips, he was still a handsome man, and evidently, to judge from his portrait, good humoured. He was now, however, a lonely man, a stranger in a strange country in which he knew no one—though he had some introductions, to be sure, to some of his countrymen who had lived there for many years. Perhaps, from his days at Leipzig, he knew something of the language—there is no record of his ever having had any difficulty on that score—but he had little money. With him, however, he brought all his determination, and the experience he had gained in working out and building his printing machine at Suhl.

Among his introductions was a man called John Hunnemann, a bookseller or librarian, who had lived in London for many years. Koenig probably went to him directly, and it may have been through the influence of Hunnemann that he presently got employment, perhaps as a compositor, in a printing office in Poland Street, off Oxford Street. This took care of his living expenses for the time being, and he began to look around him. He soon found another job, this time in a German library which had been founded by a compatriot called Weisse.

But this was not what Koenig had come to London for. He busied himself in seeking interest for his ideas. It was perhaps through Hunnemann that he came into contact with Thomas Bensley, for Hunnemann was probably the unnamed man who accompanied Koenig to an interview with the printer.

Thomas Bensley was one of the most notable printers in the country in his day. He had premises in Bolt Court, just off Fleet Street. He met Koenig and his friend on the 12th of March 1807, and listened with interest to the Saxon's ideas for a new kind of printing machine, and to his proposals for putting his ideas into practice. Bensley was a practical man, and a man who knew the value of money; he was, in fact, close to the point of dishonesty; but he saw in Koenig a man who knew what he was talking about, a man, moreover, who might give him a great advantage over rival printers, and he agreed to help in finding the money necessary to finance the invention. Koenig must have been overjoyed to hear this, to feel that he had achieved at last the first step towards success. And so he had, though he could not tell at that time how much distress and anxiety, as well as success, his alliance with Bensley was to bring.

An agreement was drawn up between Koenig and Bensley and witnessed by Hunnemann. Bensley agreed to purchase the invention if it fulfilled its promise; or, if he did not buy it, promised not to divulge any part of it, under pain of a penalty of six thousand pounds.

This turned out to be only a preliminary agreement, for there followed discussions on costs and on the benefits to be derived from the invention when it was complete. Chickens were counted before they were hatched a dozen times over, and Koenig himself was jubilant after so many reverses. With all the discussions going on, and the great sums of money that were mentioned from time to time, he must have felt at the heart of the thing at last, and he saw ahead into a rosy future. He wrote to his mother to tell her that he was now in legal association with one of the principal printers of England, and that he was to have half of the benefits of his invention, a matter which would give him an income of some six thousand thalers. Koenig was already a rich man in his own estimation; but if he did not already know it he was to learn the force of the English proverb about the cup and the lip. Bensley was to prove good at promises, but he was a wily man with a rooted aversion to paying money to anybody.

It was soon clear that the amount of money that would be needed to develop the machine was more than Bensley himself cared to put into the venture, and he sought for others to come into association with himself and Koenig. The obvious man to go to in such a case was John Walter, the proprietor of *The Times*, then the greatest newspaper in the country. Walter had felt for years the pinch between the slow, traditional methods of printing and the growing demands of the circulation of his newspaper, and everyone knew it. If anyone should be interested in a new and faster printing machine, then surely Walter was the man. But Walter had had some of this before. Koenig was not the first by any means to think of inventing a printing machine, and all those predecessors who had thought they had done it or could do it had gone to Walter for the very same reasons that Bensley went now. Walter had tried some of the ideas, and had lost money. Indeed, one such event had just occurred, so that Bensley could scarcely have come at a worse time. Walter was in no mind to take on another speculation, and the printer came away from Times Square empty handed. It was a misfortune for Koenig. If Walter had come into the agreement, he would surely have kept Bensley in hand, and Koenig would have been richer.

However, Bensley found two other men to join him, two fellow printers, George Woodfall and Richard Taylor, and an agreement was drawn up between the four partners on the 29th of November 1809. This stated that Bensley had already advanced £500 to Koenig for the purposes of his invention, and that Woodfall and Taylor agreed to advance a like sum, not at once, but piecemeal as it was demanded, and that in the end they would share in proportion to the amount they had actually advanced. If they advanced the maximum, then three-eighths of the investment were to belong to them. Bensley would have three-eighths also. The remaining share was to be Koenig's. There were some other provisions, among which was an undertaking to repay to Koenig the money he had spent in the development of the printing machine before he came to England. This was calculated at £1060. If the new machine, served by one man to feed the sheets and another to take them off, failed to reach a speed of three hundred sheets per hour, then Koenig would get none of his £1060. If the machine reached a speed between 200 and 350 sheets per hour, then he would get a third of the sum. If the speed was between 350 and 400, then he would receive two-thirds. If 400 sheets per hour was reached, then the whole sum was to be paid.

A further condition provided for a payment of ten pounds per month to Koenig while the invention was in progress.

Another, and fateful, condition spoke of the proceeds of the sales of the machines, or *of not putting them on sale at all.* If the latter alternative were adopted, then of course any advantages that the machines might have would be confined to the three printers who were parties to the agreement. This short-sighted and self-centred clause was evidently Bensley's, for it was Bensley alone who, in the event, attempted to benefit by it. It seems not to have occurred to Koenig that his invention, if it were successful, would not spread throughout the world.

It is in this agreement that for the first time we come upon the name of Andre Frederick Bauer, mentioned as a friend of Koenig's. Bauer was a compatriot, a trained engineer, and henceforth he was to be associated with Koenig throughout the rest of his life. Just what Bauer did or was in the Koenig organization has not, however, been wholly clear. Certainly he was Koenig's right hand, the second in command. It is probable that Bauer was responsible for many of the engineering devices embodied in the inventions, devices and principles with which, as an engineer, he would be familiar, but which were not as well known to Koenig. It appears that, though Koenig was always the moving spirit, the man with ideas, the two were a team indispensable one to the other.

There is no more information about the progress of the machine on which they were working, no other agreements, no letters, no contemporary accounts. Koenig was perhaps too busy to write about what he was doing, and some of the very few documents that survive from this period are letters from the indefatigable and ever hopeful Riedel asking for news of his money. There was probably reason for keeping back information. Automatic machines that did away with the necessity for workmen were not popular, and there had been riots and damage on many occasions in other trades when such things were introduced; there was nothing to

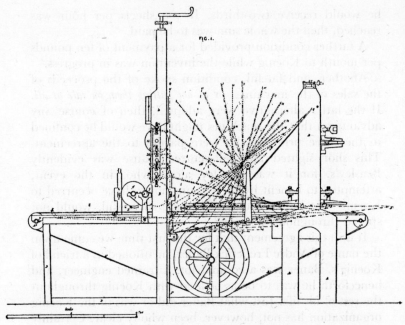

36. Koenig's 1810 machine, the first metal printing machine.
Another mechanized hand-press, based on the Suhl machine. The
dotted 'windmill' lines show the movement of the tympan and
the frisket. The inking system has a screw handle at the top to
regulate flow or pressure.

suggest that printers were going to be any more docile than
weavers and spinners, if they got to know what was going on.

A patent was applied for in March 1810. The machine
was to be an adaptation of the machine built at Suhl, but it
was to be made of iron instead of wood, and with minor
improvements that were meant to improve the working of
the parts. One of these was the introduction of two inking
rollers in contact with the forme, instead of the single one of
the Suhl machine. The idea of a roller for inking the type,
instead of the old ink ball, though in the right direction,
always gave Koenig a lot of trouble. It was clearly only by
rollers that automatic inking could ever be attained, but the
problem was to find a suitable material to cover them. The
ink balls used with the hand-press were covered with leather,

which in some factories was soaked in water or in urine until it was soft, a state in which it was supposed to be more receptive to ink, but which made the press-room stink. Leather seemed, by precedent, to be the obvious material to consider for covering rollers. Koenig used a prepared sheepskin, and to prevent this from going hard, as it was certain to do, it was fastened on a roller with a hollow spindle with perforations through to the surface. Steam was forced through the spindle, and so through the perforations into the leather, which was thus kept in good condition throughout the run. It does not sound as though this elaborate idea could possibly have worked.

The machine did work, however, and with complete success, to win the whole of the sum of £1060. The speed of four hundred sheets per hour was achieved without difficulty, and Koenig seemed to be triumphant.

Perhaps he felt so after all the years of rebuff and obstruction, after all the difficulties, delays, and contempt. But perhaps he realized also that the machine he had invented was in fact a dead end, merely an adaptation. He was already at work on a new and much more advanced machine. He saw that the up-and-down movement of the hand-press which he had preserved in his first Suhl machine and retained in his English machine was indeed an obstacle to further progress. He perceived that just as he had simplified and speeded up the inking system by means of a roller, he might also speed up the impression by means of a cylinder instead of a platen. In part it was the same as Nicholson's idea, and Koenig may have read Nicholson's patent; even if he had, his new machine could not be said to be derived from that patent. Nicholson had proposed to put his type on the face of a second cylinder, and Koenig proposed to leave it on the flat bed of the press. The bed in the first two machines had been made to reciprocate, to move in and out from under the platen, and this kind of movement was to be retained, with a cylinder in place of the platen to press the paper into contact with the type. Koenig seems to have thought this out before the first machine was finished; he began to build it as soon as that machine was out of the way.

It was patented in October 1811, and was ready to be put into operation in December 1812. Koenig and Bauer now had a workshop of their own in White Cross Street, and this no doubt enabled them to push ahead with their work with more freedom and greater dispatch. The machine was set up in the workshop, and invitations were sent to various interested and notable people who might like to see it in action, and might also prove to be possible customers. Among those invited was Perry of the *Morning Post* and John Walter of *The Times*. Walter still sought a machine to print his newspaper, despite the disillusion he had experienced previously, and perhaps he came now because he knew that the first machine built by Koenig in England had been successful and was still in production in Bensley's office. Perhaps this ingenious Saxon had achieved success again, perhaps he now had a machine that would solve the production problems of *The Times*.

The thing they had come to see stood gauntly in the middle

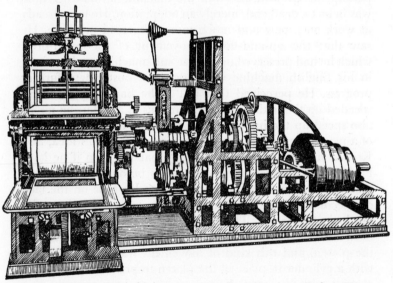

37. The first cylinder printing machine, made in 1812. The mass of mechanism at the right is the drive system, larger than the printing machine itself.

of the floor in the workshop, which must have been cleared and cleaned for this great occasion. A steam engine puffed away beside it. Presently the printing machine was started and sheets were fed through it by one man, to be removed, as they were printed, by a second man. Without effort a speed of over eight hundred sheets per hour was reached, sheets larger than could easily be printed on a hand-press at a tenth of the speed. Walter was impressed and completely won over. Not so Perry. The man from the *Morning Post* could see no point in spending the great amount of money the machine would cost simply to speed up the printing of a morning paper. The old hand-press was good enough for him. Walter was a far shrewder man, and with more fore-sight. He knew, as he always had, that a successful printing machine would revolutionize not only the machine-room of the newspaper, but the composing room also. At that time the newspaper was printed on a battery of hand-presses, each with two men; and to provide for each press, and to get the newspaper out on time, the compositors had to set up the copy several times over. The more the circulation of the paper grew, the greater the number of presses that had to be employed, and the more times the type had to be set. A machine that ran at several times the speed of the hand-press would not only produce more newspapers during the night, and so dispense with the hand-presses, it would also mean that the type could be set up fewer times, and so reduce the costs in the composing room. There was no doubt that a successful machine, even if the the price were high, would pay for itself very soon.

Walter talked with Koenig about his new machine, a Koenig a little shy of this great man, very likely, and flattered to have his unqualified approval. He told Walter of his plans, now maturing, to build yet another printing machine, which would produce still more sheets in the hour than the one they had before them. This new machine was to be larger, and it was to have two cylinders, one of which would print a sheet as the bed moved one way, and the other another sheet as the bed returned. It could not produce twice as much as the single-cylinder machine—Koenig knew that—but it would certainly produce more. Walter was convinced and enthusiastic, and he ordered two of these machines on the spot.

Work was begun at once on this new equipment for *The Times*, and the workshop in White Cross Street was busy. It had, however, to be done in secret. It was essential that the workers in *The Times* office should not hear of it, for if they did there would certainly be trouble there. If the knowledge leaked out to the trade in general, it was Koenig and his machines that might suffer, for by this time he was not popular with printers, who thought that he threatened their livelihood with his demoniac apparatus. They had already seen the effect of the introduction of machines into other industries, and they could scarcely be blamed for resenting the hardship they had undoubtedly caused. There was still rife plenty of the feeling that had resulted in the destruction of the spinning jenny and the weaving frame by workmen made violent by fear of starvation. Koenig had been threatened several times, not only with the destruction of those contraptions of his that took the bread from men's mouths, but also with danger to himself. He did not take these threats too seriously, but at least it was wise, and imperative for Walter's sake, not to flaunt his achievements in the market place. There was still another danger that Koenig risked, one that he must have feared more than any other, and which was not understood by the printers who threatened his machine. If the new machine for *The Times* proved to be a failure, if it did not work for whatever reason, the howl of mockery and ridicule that would go up from the trade would endanger his entire future. These machines had to be right first time.

The workmen in the factory in White Cross Street were bound, under a penalty of a hundred pounds each, not to divulge anything they knew or learned about the work going on there. It is unlikely that they knew the full importance of the machines they were building, or the destination they were intended for, but surely in the end they put two and two together and worked it out for themselves. Perhaps a visit from Walter to the workshop, an overheard remark here and a hint there, and they were in possession of the facts. Still, it did not leak out to the pressmen of *The Times*, or if they did hear of it, it was no important matter and peace was preserved.

Because of this necessity for secrecy, this need to avoid trouble from the employees of the newspaper, it was clearly out of the question to set up the machinery in *The Times* building in the first instance. It would have been torn down

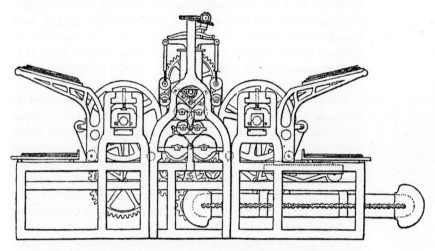

38. The double feeder machine built for *The Times* and first put into operation in 1814. Sheets were fed from the feeding board at each end and were carried round the cylinder, to be taken off on the delivery tables beneath the feeding boards. The inking system is in the centre.

or damaged as fast as it was built. It was essential that it should be set up and working before anything was known, so that the men would in fact be presented with a *fait accompli*. A building not far from Printing House Square was obtained, and with great caution the parts of the machine were conveyed to this place, at night or at other times when it was safe. Towards the end of November 1814 the machine was ready, a monster by contemporary standards, waiting to eat up paper. The paper had probably been delivered in small lots from time to time, and all that was needed now was the formes. These had to come from *The Times* building. There the pressmen were standing by their Stanhopes, waiting for the formes to print them off. They were told to go on waiting because important dispatches were on the way from the Continent, where the Napoleonic wars were going on, rather as though, as far as this story is concerned, they had been taking place on another planet. So the little army of pressmen and their assistants waited, impatiently at first, no doubt, and then resigned, smoking, playing cards, falling asleep, cursing the management, and probably glad of their respite from labour. Did they at last begin to wonder, to become suspicious, as the time passed by and they knew that by this, whatever the news, the paper would never be printed by the morning.

But it was being printed then. Walter had managed to smuggle a set of formes out of his office and into the temporary machine-room where Koenig and Bauer waited for it with their workmen, and soon the cylinders of the great machine were turning with full vigour and *The Times* was coming off the press at a speed unprecedented in all the history of printing. There were no reservations about it. The machine was a complete success. The triumph of the inventor and the pride of the newspaper proprietor are reflected in the first article of the issue of the 29th of November, in which the new method of printing the newspaper is described.

Who set this article, written by Walter, which gave the whole show away, or would have done if it had got into the hands of the compositors in the composing room of *The Times*? Did Walter himself take off his coat and set to work at the frame? It is possible.

At six o'clock in the morning Walter went into his press-room with some of the newspapers in his hand. By this time the men must have known that something was up, something serious, too, to have prevented them from printing the day's issue of the paper. There must have been anxious discussion, worried surmise, and the appearance of the proprietor would tell them that at last they were about to know.

Walter was aware that he was taking some risk, but he had provided for trouble. The issue of *The Times*, he told the men, had been worked off in the night by a new machine powered by steam, and the newspaper would be printed so in the future. This announcement might well have been followed by a riot, but Walter continued: he would not have any disorder, he said; if there was any attempt, he had force at hand sufficient to suppress it. If, however, the men took his news calmly, and no mischief was attempted against the new machinery, then every man would be paid his full wages until such time as he found a job elsewhere. This was a fair offer, and probably the men realized that it was so. There was no trouble, no demonstration.

In the article in *The Times*, Walter wrote:

'Our journal of this day presents to the public the practical result of the greatest improvement connected with printing, since the discovery of the art itself. The reader of this paragraph now holds in his hands one of the many thousands of impressions of *The Times* newspaper, which were taken off last night by a mechanical apparatus. A system of machinery almost organic has been devised and arranged, which, while it relieves the human frame from the most laborious efforts in printing, far exceeds all human power in rapidity and dispatch. That the magnitude of the invention may be duly appreciated by its effects, we shall inform the public, that after the letters are placed by the compositors, and enclosed in what is called the forme, little more remains for man to do than to attend upon, and watch this unconscious agent in its operations. This machine is then merely supplied with paper: itself places the forme, inks it, adjusts the paper to the forme newly inked, stamps the sheets, and gives it forth to the hands of the attendant, at the same time withdrawing the forme for a fresh coat of ink, which itself again distributes, to meet the ensuing sheet now advancing for impression; and the whole of these complicated acts is performed with such a velocity and simultaneousness of movement, that no less than eleven hundred sheets are impressed in one hour.

'That the completion of an invention of this kind, not the effect of chance, but the result of mechanical combinations methodically arranged in the mind of the artist, should be attended with many and much delay may be readily admitted. Our share in this event, has, indeed, only been the application of the discovery, under an agreement with the Patentees, to our own particular business: but few can conceive—even with this limited interest—the various disappointments and the deep anxiety to which we have for a long course of time been subjected.

'Of the person who made this discovery, we have but little to add. *Sir Christopher Wren's* noblest monument is to be found in the buildings which he erected; so is the best tribute of praise, which we are capable of offering to the inventor of the Printing Machine, comprised in the preceding description, which we have feebly sketched, of the powers and ability of this invention. It must suffice to say further, that he is a Saxon by birth; that his name is Koenig, and that the invention has been executed under the direction of his friend and countryman Bauer.'

With the single cylinder machine patented in 1811 and the machines built for *The Times*, the invention of the printing machine may be said to be complete, demonstrably successful. The day of the hand-press, however it might linger still in small offices, was over. No printing house equipped with hand-presses could compete with one equipped with one of the Koenig and Bauer machines, or one of those that developed from them. The change could not be immediate, for there were comparatively few printers large enough to be able to afford the new equipment, nor was there yet a sufficiently large demand for print for the machines to become widespread quickly. The cost of them was great, and must have been deterrent. A printer had to contemplate an expenditure something in the region of a thousand pounds for one machine, and in Koenig's day that was a considerable sum of money.

There was also another obstacle to the spread of the invention. Bensley opposed the sale of machines generally. He thought that they ought to be confined to his own office, with only one or two exceptions. Unfortunately he could force this policy on his partners, for one of the original three printers had dropped out, and Bensley had very quickly

snapped up his shares. This purchase gave him the controlling interest.

Bensley proved altogether a miserable partner for Koenig.
The printer played all sorts of tricks, and made every kind of
excuse, to avoid paying to Koenig money he owed to him as
a result of the agreements they had signed together; and
further he made claims against the inventor which can only
be described as impudent.

Things had to go all his own way to be considered equit-
able by Bensley. Although he opposed the manufacture and
general sale of the Koenig machines, he had no compunction

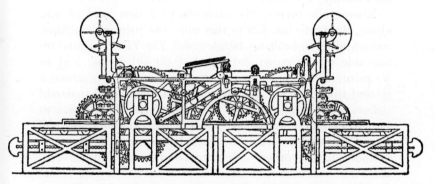

39. Koenig's perfecting machine of 1816, which printed both sides
of the paper in one operation.

in allowing other engineers into his office to study those that
he had. This was flatly against the agreements, but Bensley
worked on the principle that what he wanted to do was
right, and what other people wanted to do was wrong if he
did not like it. Among the engineers he called in was Applegath, who, later with Cowper, began to build machines in
competition with Koenig and Bauer. Protests from Koenig
were ignored, and the efforts of Taylor, the remaining
partner, were feeble and served no better.

Despite all these annoyances and impediments, Koenig's
busy mind was full of new ideas, all designed to increase the
scope and speed of his machines. One of his ideas was a
fantastic and enormous machine with a bed in the form of a

137

ring, large enough to hold several formes. Riding on this bed there were to be no less than eight conical cylinders, and as many inking systems and feeding tables. The idea was that as the circular bed went round, carrying the formes, each of these would in turn print a sheet under each of the cylinders—eight sheets per cylinder for each revolution, and eight cylinders, equals sixty-four sheets in one revolution of the bed. This mammoth was never built, and perhaps it was impossible, but it was no more extraordinary than some of the giants that were built for the newspapers later, in the never-ending attempt to squeeze more and more impressions into less and less time.

Koenig also turned his attention to a new kind of machine, the perfector. Up to this time any printing machine, including those built for Bensley and *The Times*, printed on one side of the paper only, and if the other side had to be printed, then the sheet must go through the machine a second time. Koenig now attempted a machine that would deliver a sheet fully printed in one traverse. There were to be two cylinders, rather as in *The Times* examples, and the paper followed a serpentine path between cords from one cylinder to the other, emerging completely printed. This machine was built and erected in Bensley's works, where it proved entirely successful, producing over a thousand printed sheets per hour. This was a remarkable achievement, though it added no new principle to the invention of the printing machine.

In all Koenig's machines the paper was held against the cylinder by endless cords, which took the sheet as it was fed and controlled it until it was delivered. This system held the paper all right, but it did not allow it to be placed exactly, which made register somewhat uncertain. This was not improved until metal grippers were introduced, not by Koenig, some years later.

Another development of the printing machine due to Koenig is the two-revolution press. Previous machines, like modern stop cylinders, had cylinders that ceased to revolve while the bed was on the return stroke. Koenig's two-revolution machine was made so that the cylinder continued to revolve, probably with some saving in vibration. This kind of machine does not seem to have had any great vogue at that time.

Koenig was now disgusted with his treatment by Bensley, and particularly with the obstacles he placed in the way of the sales of the machines. The printer seemed to be a permanent hindrance, preventing the expansion of the invention throughout the printing industry and by this means also interfering with Koenig's fortune. Perhaps, too, the Saxon was becoming homesick. He had so often written to his mother, to send her money, and had heard from her sometimes, too. He had frequently told her that some day he would return. Now the wars were over at last, and if he wanted to return it would not be difficult. He was not a rich man, but he was not a poor one either, and he could afford to travel. But he meant to do more than merely to visit his native country. He and Bauer decided that they would return there for good, find a place for a factory, and build printing machines freely and sell them where they could. In July 1817 he wrote to his mother, now an old woman of eighty, to say that at last the time had come, and that in a few days he would depart for Germany.

It was nearly twelve years since he had left his native country, and since he had seen his mother last. The old lady seemed to have hung on to life simply to see again the successful son who had so often promised to come home, and now was arrived at last. Each of them must have seemed to the other to have grown much older; and the world was different too, older, stranger, harder. Koenig was now over forty, burly and vigorous, but not strong. He had several times been ill in England, and seriously so during the building of his first machine. He did his utmost not to allow this to interfere with his activities, however, and in Germany he was soon in search of what he had come for, a site for the new factory he and Bauer intended to open in their own country. He looked for suitable buildings in a suitable environment. Many years before, he remembered, he had seen at Oberzell, near Wurzburg, a monastery of Premonstratensian monks, abandoned and falling into ruin, with large buildings strongly walled, containing the great halls and rooms which were what he wanted. He went there to see it, and found the place much as it had been, untenanted, with only a pair of old men to look after it, and after the gardens which surrounded it. Neither of them, evidently, did his work as it should have been done, and the effect was depressing, frowzy with decay and neglect.

Koenig saw beyond the disadvantages and decided that this was the place he wanted. It belonged to the crown, and Koenig proposed to lease the monastery. His proposal was received with such favour, however, in the Bavarian court, to which his application came, that alternative proposals were made to him. The court was proud to have the inventor of the printing machine in its territory, would be honoured if he settled there and started his factory. The monastery was offered for sale to him at a very low price, and Koenig soon found himself the owner of this great range of buildings, with more space than he thought he would ever need. He wrote to tell Bauer, who had remained in London to look after their affairs there, about Oberzell.

The problem of turning a monastery in an agricultural district into a factory was more difficult than Koenig had hoped it would be. It was a rash idea, at the best, to attempt to train engineering staff from a people who for centuries had known only the growing of vines and the making of wine, the tending of cattle and the ploughing of land. The men came to Koenig from villages and farms, wherever they could be got, presumably to earn higher wages than they could get in the work they were used to. It needed patience and tact to turn these countrymen into engineers, foundrymen, turners, and so forth. I suspect that it was better when Bauer came from England, for the faithful Bauer, always in the background, modest, perhaps shy, was more knowledgeable in engineering, and was probably a better teacher.

They soon had orders, from their own country, from Russia, from England, and possibly some from America. It seemed that the new factory was going to be busy. There were disappointments, as there were bound to be, and there were hard times, when orders were scarce and money difficult to come by. Slowly the teething troubles were overcome, and the factory began to flourish, despite difficulties that the partners had not foreseen, or if they had foreseen them, had underestimated. For instance, the coke for melting the iron in the furnaces had to come all the way from England, and the best iron also had to come from the same source. Further, they had to go to England for the steam engines to drive their machines, for nothing good enough was to be had on the Continent. An engine of one horse-power cost £120; one of two horse-power £220; and one of four horse-power £350. All these things were heavy and cost a good deal to move, and this must have been reflected in the price of the printing machines. There were difficulties of a different kind with crass or obstructionist customs officials when completed machines had to be sent through one country to another.

It was no doubt partly because of the cost of the engines that Koenig and Bauer produced a cylinder machine which could be operated by the power of one or two workmen turning a handle on the flywheel.

Once they were established in Oberzell and they felt that their business was running well, Koenig and Bauer began to consider whether they should get married. These two solid German gentlemen, bachelors until now, seem to have decided entirely on grounds of logic that they ought to have wives. It may be that they realized that there ought to be someone to inherit the firm when they died, or perhaps they felt at last, now that they had a little more leisure, the need for feminine companionship. They seem to have set out to look for wives like someone going for a pound of tea or a new coat.

All those years ago, before the wars and before he had achieved any success, Koenig had been in love with Johanna Hoffmann in Suhl. He remembered her, indeed, had been to see her. She, poor girl, had been forced into a marriage she did not relish, and now she lived with a family of children, a widow with little means. If Koenig had carried the youthful picture of her in his head, it must surely have been shattered when he saw her again, a woman worn out by poverty and the struggle to keep her children. If she in turn thought that the Koenig of old might return to her, she too was

141

disappointed, for he paid her no more attention now than courtesy and kindliness warranted. He helped her, it seems.

Johanna had an eldest daughter, just now growing into womanhood, in whom Koenig was interested, though not at first as a possible wife. He was busy wooing a girl at Wurzburg who appeared to have all the qualities he asked for. Koenig was duly recognized as her suitor and was a frequent visitor to her house. What he did not know, and was certainly not told by her parents, was that she suffered at times from what Koenig later described as a temporary eclipse of her faculties. He saw her in one of these states, which her mother and elder sister tried to conceal from him. The girl herself told Koenig all about it, in a moment when her guardians were out of the way. As soon as they knew that Koenig was aware of the girl's defect, her parents pressed him to make his decision at once. They did not want to give him any time to think. The suitor managed to escape, and a few days later he sent to them a disturbed and sad letter to say that he could no longer pay suit to the girl. The decision upset him, and he wrote to Bauer for his advice on whether he had acted honourably and humanely.

Koenig was fifty when he proposed marriage to Fanny Jacobs, the daughter of Johanna Hoffmann. Fanny was seventeen. Since she was heart-whole, and the marriage would help her mother, she consented, but she seems also to have been genuinely fond of the man who was old enough to be her father. They were married in October 1825. Like many other such ill-assorted marriages, this one was a success, and the two lived happily enough together. The children who would carry on the name duly arrived, first two sons and then a daughter.

Koenig never ceased to be deeply interested in the progress of printing, and he was frequently off in pursuit of new ideas, as he had always been. He pushed on with his experiments in stereotyping, for instance, and he also considered the possibility of a composing machine. This idea was mentioned to him by someone, and his first reaction was amusement. He thought, as many others did later that the nimble movements of the compositor's fingers could never be duplicated by a machine. A few days later, however, he thought differently. He had given the idea some attention, and it seemed to him now that it might be done; but he had neither the apparatus nor the personnel at Oberzell to undertake the delicate work that would be required for the making of the parts. The composing machine was put aside.

Koenig still had business ties with London, and once or twice again came to England to see about his affairs. He evidently did not go to see Bensley at these times, though he no doubt went to see John Walter. On one of these visits Bensley heard that he was in the city and inquired of Taylor for his address. Bensley stated that he had some claims to make on Koenig. Taylor, who knew that Bensley had repeatedly failed to pay moneys owing to the inventor, was astonished, and reminded Bensley of what he owed. The printer said gruffly that he could not remember anything about that. Bensley was altogether an unlovable character, at odds with even his own son. The printing house in Bolt Court was burned down in a disastrous fire, and the printer was left with nothing of all his fine equipment. He moved elsewhere and set up a small printing office, apparently with hand-presses. His son salvaged the machinery from the burned building, and found that some of it which had been in the basement could be put into order again. He now turned the full competitive power of the printing machine against his father's small business, and made the father feel what he must have made other printers feel when he endeavoured to keep the advantages of the printing machine to himself. The younger Bensley prospered until, as avaricious as his father, he thought he could make his fortune quickly on the stock exchange. He sold the business and bought shares with the money, and began a career of investment and share gambling which in the end ruined him.

As he grew older Koenig's health weakened. He began to suffer severely from vertigo and insomnia, and in January 1833 he had an apoplectic fit. Two days later, on the 17th, he died. Bauer lived on until 1860, carrying on the firm with success. It is still in existence.

3. DEVELOPMENT AFTER KOENIG

Koenig's departure from England was not, it was to prove, a major loss to the development of the printing machine in this country. Before he left these shores the inventor saw other men building upon the basis of what he had himself conceived, and building printing machines in competition with him, or improving details of existing designs until they reached a peak of efficiency greatly in advance of the early machines. A number of capable engineers were engaged in studying and developing the printing machine to meet an ever increasing demand, and among them, in England, were Bryan Donkin, Robert Harrild, and Applegath and Cowper. Newspapers competed with one another to expand their circulations and to publish later and later news, and this competition fostered the development of enormous machines of many cylinders, needing eight, ten, or twelve men to feed them and to remove the sheets when they were printed. With all these hands, speeds of ten or twelve thousand copies per hour were reached.

Still it was not enough. The multiplication of cylinders and men could not go on indefinitely, and there had to be some alternative method of getting out the vast quantities the reading public now came to need. It was clear that the method developed by Koenig, that is to say, the printing of single sheets on a machine on which the type lay flat on a reciprocating bed, would not do any longer for newspaper production, and ingenious engineers turned their attention to the rotary principle suggested by Nicholson years before. How conscious they were of Nicholson's ideas, it is not easy to say. The need had arrived, and the idea was in the air. One of the most difficult problems of such a machine was how to fasten the type to the surface of a cylinder so that it would neither fall off nor fly off by the force of centrifugal motion. Nicholson's solution of this almost certainly would not work, but the problem was solved, in several ways, and machines put into motion in which the type, on the face of a cylinder, printed paper which was fed between it and another cylinder. Most of these machines in fact printed from a cylinder which was rather a polyhedron, since it was so arranged that each column of type, running the length of the cylinder, was flat. These machines printed, though they must have given a good deal of trouble.

The real solution of the problem was the invention of stereotyping, made some years before, but now adapted to

40. The four-cylinder, four-feeder press built by Applegath and Cowper for *The Times*. Four more men were needed to lift the printed sheets from the cylinders.

produce a curved plate which could be clamped on the surface of the cylinder. Stereotyping began as a method of duplicating a forme by making a mould from it and using the mould to cast a sheet or block of metal with the characters on one face, which could then be used for printing. A method of doing it had been invented early in the eighteenth century by William Ged and successfully torpedoed by interests that conceived themselves threatened by it. Stanhope, later, had developed a method, and Koenig had some kind of process of his own. As soon as stereotyping could be made to produce a cast with a predetermined and accurate radius, the problem of fixing a printing surface to a cylinder was solved for good. It is the method used today in every great newspaper printing works in the world, in conjunction with enormous machines that cope with the fantastic circulations of modern newspapers.

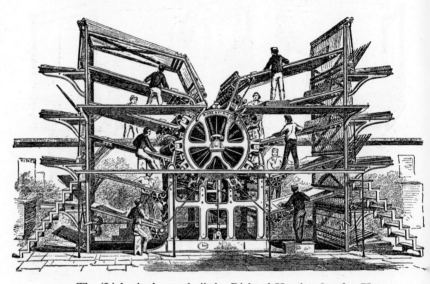

41. The 'Lightning' press built by Richard Hoe in 1857 for *The Times*. This enormous machine carried the type fixed round the periphery of the large central cylinder, and ten feeders fed vast sheets of paper to it.

Machines of such high speeds could never depend on the limitations of hand-feeding of single sheets. With two cylinders revolving one against the other, and the paper passing between them, it was clear that it should be possible to feed the paper continuously through from a reel, from which the individual copies could be cut after printing. The arrival of such a machine meant the end of the gigantic multiple feeders on which the newspapers had depended until now.

The rapid increase in the speed of printing produced new

146

difficulties after printing. Newspapers had to be folded, and hand-folding meant the employment of crowds of girls. Folding was now the bottleneck through which every copy had to pass, and at which production was dammed up. The answer was, of course, another machine, the folding machine, and when this was combined with the rotary printing press, the newspaper publisher had at his command a single, though compound, machine that would print, separate, and fold the newspapers, and, eventually, deliver them counted in quires.

Plant of this kind was not needed by the jobbing printer, who was seldom concerned with quantities of this nature. What he wanted was a machine that would print well at a moderate speed, a thousand to two thousand per hour, that would give good register, and that was adaptable quickly to various kinds of work, taking a couple of hundred of one job in the morning, and a few thousand on a different size of sheet in the afternoon. Koenig's first cylinder machine was just the thing, and equipment of this kind soon began to be common in printing houses throughout the civilized world. Most of these machines were powered by engines of one kind or another, but in some works they were turned by a labourer, and a tough and back-breaking job it must have been.

The cylinder and reciprocating bed gave very much better quality than any rotary machine, and the conception was in general so fundamentally sound that it remains the basis of printing machine design to the present day. The stop cylinder, the machine in which the cylinder ceases to revolve while the bed is making its return stroke, proved to be the most popular at first, and for many years. One of the reasons for this was the production of a new kind of stop-cylinder machine by two partners who started a factory in Otley in Yorkshire, in the valley of the Wharfe. Their machine was simple, efficient, and economic, and so durable that there are still many examples at work in printing houses that were made more than fifty years ago. Its popularity was such that machines of its type, whether made in Otley or elsewhere, are now called Wharfedales.

The two-revolution press, a variety of which had also been

developed by Koenig, did not become as popular until the arrival of a machine developed by Robert Miehle towards the end of the century. The printer of today may choose excellent machines of either kind from a wide variety. The larger examples, used for printing books and magazines, are generally two-revolution machines of the Miehle kind, but among the smaller ones there is lively competition between the two varieties.

42. An early Wharfedale press, with an engine to drive it. The paper passes round the large cylinder clockwise, round the smaller one anti-clockwise, and so on to the flyer sticks, which hinge backwards and forwards, delivering the sheets to the pile at the rear. This delivery system removed the need for a man to take off the printed sheets. Most Wharfedales are fed from the side opposite to this one.

The double cylinder machine of the kind made by Koenig for *The Times* has long ago vanished, but two kinds of double cylinder machine remain and may be encountered in large printing houses. One is the perfector, designed to print both sides of the sheet in the single traverse of the paper, and the other is the two-colour press, which prints two colours on one side of the paper.

Modern cylinder machines, with automatic feeders incorporated, work at speeds up to five thousand copies per hour for the smaller machines, and up to about two thousand five hundred for the larger ones. They could not do this

43. The machine room of an American printing house about 1883. With a variety of large and small machines running at a thousand and more per hour, this firm was capable of a considerable output.

without automatic feeders, for no human hand could cope with such output. Automatic feeders have now been developed to a high pitch of efficiency, and they will feed the presses with sheet after sheet at the high speeds required. They are geared to the press so that the sheets are presented as required. If a sheet is misfed for any reason, the press is automatically stopped.

The successful development of cylinder presses dealt with the mounting demands for print, but they nevertheless left a large amount of jobbing work untouched. It was still absurd to print a small handbill on a cylinder machine, and it was quite impossible to print such a thing as a visiting card. Work that could not be done on the cylinder press went to the hand-press, as it had done before, and it was not until the sixties that the position was altered. An American called Gordon saw the need for a small and fast press that would be versatile enough to deal with the wide variety of small jobs that come into the printing house, and particularly into the country printing house, and he set himself to design something to meet the need. His idea was what has now come to be called the platen machine. The forme was clipped to a vertical bed, facing a strong flat plate, the platen, on which the paper was fed to guides or lays. The bed and the platen then closed together. As they did so, a set of rollers ran up between them and up on to an inking disk, where they recharged themselves with ink, ready to roll down again as soon as the bed and the platen separated. This cycle of operations was repeated for each copy. The machine was operated by a treadle, or by power, and worked at a speed of about eight hundred to a thousand copies per hour, though an adept feeder might considerably exceed this. The sheets were fed with one hand and removed with the other.

One of Gordon's early machines earned the nickname of the Crocodile, because of its propensity for snapping at the hands of the feeder. Battered and crushed fingers marked the man who had come off worst from such an encounter.

The first Gordon platen to be seen in England was an improvement on the Crocodile. It appeared at the exhibition

44. Gordon's Franklin platen machine, here being operated by
treadle. Inking is automatic from the circular disk, from which the
rollers run down over the type between impressions.

of 1862 and attracted a good deal of attention. Later it was
manufactured in England under the name of the Minerva,
and thenceforward it rapidly made its way into printing
houses of all kinds throughout the country. The larger houses
found it an economical method of dealing with short runs
which were a nuisance on the cylinder machines, and large
and small houses found it invaluable for printing all kinds of
small work, and the only useful method of printing cards,
which would not bend round the surface of a cylinder.
Quality could be first class, and register was perfect.

It was not an expensive machine—much cheaper than a
cylinder press—and as power was by no means essential and
it could be treadled and operated by a boy, it became the

stand-by of the smallest of print shops, the machine by which they made their living. The hand-press lost by the advance of Gordon's platen its last hold in the machine-room.

Platens are now made in several varieties and in various sizes, and many are made with feeders built in, to give speeds up to three or four thousand copies per hour.

THE ADVENT OF
THE COMPOSING MACHINE

A MODERN novel, a little on the long side as modern novels go, may contain a hundred thousand words, more than half a million characters. Many Victorian novels are twice as long as this, and with a larger proportion of longer words, might well come to a million and a half of characters. There may be as many, or more than this, in a daily newspaper. Every one of these characters and spaces for the nineteenth-century novel, or other book, or for a newspaper, had to be picked up by the nimble fingers of a compositor, turned the right way round, and inserted in a line of its fellows in the composing stick he held in his left hand. At the end of the line, he had to pause to adjust the spacing between the words, making it wider or narrower, to expand or compress the line until it exactly filled the measure of the stick. His speed was around a thousand to fourteen hundred characters per hour, much slower after dark, when he had to work by the light of a candle, or by the flare of a fish-tail gas jet. Alone, he might have to work for a thousand hours on a novel—sixteen to twenty weeks of work.

Half a dozen compositors working together in a group called a companionship, or 'ship, got through the novel without difficulty in a few weeks, but the situation was not the same in a newspaper office. There the matter had to be set within the day, much of it within minutes, if it was late news, and it could only be done by employing scores of compositors and vast amounts of type, so that each man could be given a part of the work that he could compass in the time.

The method of setting type by hand in the nineteenth century differed in no fundamental manner from that practised in the earliest days of printing. In four hundred years the craft of the compositor changed not one movement, not

45. The army of compositors in the composing room of the *Western Daily News* in Bristol in 1874, before composing machines had come to alter the picture.

one principle, though the interdependent craft of the pressman did change, and as the nineteenth century proceeded and invention, sparked off by Koenig, was developed, changed out of mind.

As it was with the press, no real assault was made on the development of a machine for setting type before the turn of the nineteenth century, but it was very much longer before any real measure of success was achieved. Many inventors tried their hands at the problem. Any compositor who resented the incursion of machinery into his craft, and there were many of them, might have watched with confidence the disappointing results of all these attempts, and have felt himself secure in his job.

Certainly the problems facing the inventor were severe and manifold. With capitals and lower case, figures, signs, points, and so forth, the most modest total of characters in an ordinary fount will come to something in the region of eighty; and one such fount is not really enough in itself, for italics are needed also, and small capitals, and it is desirable to have upper and lower case of bold face as well. The total on the modern Monotype machine comes to 255 characters. An inventor had to build a machine that would, under instruction from an operator working at a keyboard, select and assemble all these characters, all the right way round and the right way up and in the desired order. He also had to provide a method of justifying or spacing out the line. Few inventors attempted anything like so wide a variety of characters; most limited themselves to the eighty or so needed for one fount.

The first essay seems to have been that of an Englishman with the un-English name of Hoffman, who undertook, about 1790, a machine that would indent letters, or dies, in sequence in some kind of plastic material which would afterwards act as a mould for casting a line or page of type. He seems to have been influenced by the technique of stereotyping. This effort was a failure, and repetitions of the idea, which occurred several times in the following century, were uniformly failures. Nevertheless Hoffman's example is interesting because, in not attempting the composition of actual type, he came nearer the eventual solution of the problem than did most of those who succeeded him.

Since the general idea was to set type, it was easier to think of a machine that would handle actual type like that used by the compositor; but it was difficult to put the idea into practice. It would have been naïve to think of something that would stand at the case in place of the compositor, and which would set type in a stick in the same way; it was naïve, but amusing, and some contemporary caricatures

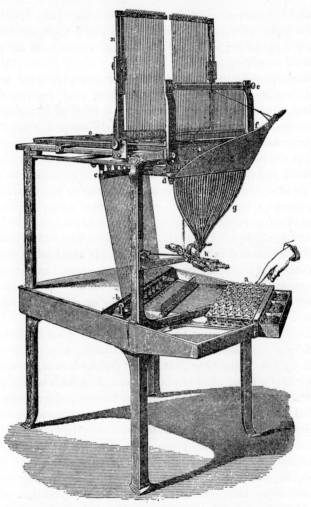

46. Hattersley's type-setting machine. It did not justify the
lines it set.

show mechanical manikins of this nature, with steam belch-
ing forth as they compose. This satyric comment reflects the
attitude of the trade to the composing machine—not really
convinced that it was possible, but afraid that it might be.

Obviously, however it was done, it could not be an easy

matter to persuade a machine to handle and move around a lot of little pieces of metal, less than an inch high and varying from a thirty-second to an eighth of an inch thick, all of which must be kept in order and the right way up. Every compositor knows how easily type can pie. But this was the problem that inventors set themselves, and some of them achieved, in one way or another, a surprising amount of success. Early in the second half of the century there were several machines in operation in printing offices. They were not, however, completely satisfactory. There were two fundamental and well-nigh insuperable problems that faced every man who tried to design a machine to use founders' type, and these were the supply of type to the machine, and the justifying of the lines when they had been set.

The supply of type caused permanent difficulties. A machine cannot take its type letter by letter from a compositor's case, divided into boxes each containing a quantity of one particular letter. Therefore the letters were gathered together and arranged in rows in slides, each slide containing one kind of character, with the first in the row, or rank, ready to be released at the touch of a controlling key. The slides had to be filled by hand, and this meant that the used type had to be distributed in the usual way into the case, and then set up again in rows ready for insertion into the slides. This entailed a great waste of time and seriously curtailed the advantage in speed that was the only reason for having a composing machine at all.

To get over the difficulty, distributing machines were developed to go with composing machines. To make them work the type had to be nicked in a special way so that each letter had a combination of nicks different from that of any other letter. The type was fed to the machine line by line, and it then sorted out the letters by their respective nicks, distributing the characters into the proper slides, ready for use on the composing machine again.

Neither distributing machines nor composing machines seem to have been completely satisfactory or dependable.

However, with his slides replenished, the operator of the composing machine was ready to start work. Following his copy, he spelled out the words on the keys until he came to the end of the line. Then came the second fundamental problem, the justification of the line of type. I have remarked that the compositor makes all his lines the same length, like those you are reading now, by increasing or reducing the spaces between the words. He does this when he has set as much of the matter as will go into the measure, when he can see whether he has room to complete the last word or to get

47. A Kastenbein typesetting machine, with its auxiliary distributing machine on the right. The typesetter operator's stool is empty, but his assistant is busy justifying the lines of type he has set. Kastenbein machines were in use for many years.

another word in. If he has some space left, but not enough to get the next word, or part of it, in, he increases the spaces between the words to drive the line out to the measure; if he needs to get in one or two letters to complete the last word in the line, but has not enough room, then he reduces the spaces between the words until they will go in. You can see the effect of this particularly in newspapers, where hasty composition and narrow measures bring in their train wide variation of spacing from line to line.

The compositor in effect justifies by going back on his tracks at the end of each line. To make a machine do this proved to be more than inventors could manage. The problem was abandoned. The operator set the copy in one continuous line, which proceeded down a chute or slide to a compositor, who performed the business of spacing into lines of the required measure.

So that all that the machine really did was to set the letters and standard spaces one after the other, leaving a good deal still to be done by hand. For newspapers, hard pressed by time, even machines as imperfect as these must have been some help. *The Times* ran a battery of Kastenbein machines for many years.

But invention did not stop there. The constantly increasing demands for books and newspapers and other kinds of printed matter, were a permanent incentive to invention. The composing room of any printer of importance was large and costly, equipped with many thousands of pounds in weight and value of founders' types, and manned by rows of men and boys in white aprons, each standing in his own place and setting away as if his life depended on it; and sometimes it did, for the men worked by the piece, and the less they did the less they earned. Each of them thought that his life did depend on his remaining at the case, piecework or not, for if there was no composing to be done, then there were no wages either. When eventually they saw machines coming in to take over the work they had always done, they did not hail them as labour-saving devices come to make life easier. They knew that they had come not only to save labour, but to save wages also, and the men naturally looked on the machines with distrust and anxiety when at last they saw that the threat they offered was real. There were riots and strikes.

The composing machines won, as in the end they were bound to do. No dispute or commotion prevented one inventor after another from pursuing the dream of the perfect composing machine, with great constancy through all kinds of heartbreak, and with great expenditure of money. There were many machines on the market in the later years of the nineteenth century, with many more projected or patented or described in the trade journals of the time. There were almost as many distributing machines.

48. In the foreground of this engraving of the machine room of the State printing house in Vienna about 1840 are a type-distributing machine and a typesetting machine with a piano keyboard of 120 keys.

Of the machines setting founder's type none was completely successful. The only exception to this is perhaps an extraordinary machine built by an American genius called Paige, with the financial assistance of Mark Twain. This machine never came on to the commercial market, and its efficiency is therefore not proved; but it was used for a time under commercial conditions, and was said to perform well.

It was a tremendous construction, eighteen feet long and

nine feet high, and weighing three tons. Twain contributed a hundred thousand dollars to its development, and was said to be the principal shareholder in the company controlling it. The Paige machine was extremely complicated, so much so that perhaps no one other than its inventor ever really

49. The Paige typesetting machine, the incredible monster that came too late. This machine could set, justify, and distribute type all at the same time.

understood it completely. It was years in the course of patenting, and was reputed to have driven two patent agents crazy and to have caused the suicide of others. It had the disastrous disadvantage of setting only one size of type, so that a separate machine was required for each size the printer used.

The Paige machine accomplished the whole business of typesetting, including justification and distributing. The type had to be specially nicked, and a page of it taken from the forme in which it had been printed could be fed in at the distributing end and was dealt with at the same time as the operator was tapping the keyboard to compose new matter.

One of the machines was at work, on trial, for several months in a newspaper office, and apparently did what it was expected to do; but that one machine had cost over a million dollars, and only one other was ever built. There was no more money in the kitty and Paige would not agree with his financial backers on conditions for further support. The result was that the Paige machine died, and the only two models constructed are now lodged in American museums.

Its loss was not serious. It does not seem possible that the Paige machine, however ingenious and however successful, could ever have become a commercial proposition. There is such a thing as being too clever by half; and the half in the Paige machine was about two tons and many thousands of dollars. But it was already out of date at the time it was completed. It was now the last quarter of the century, and the attention of those interested in composing machines was being drawn more and more in a different direction. Several inventions had been conceived, or were already in development, which would cast type as it was composed, and the men who were to solve the problem of mechanical composition, completely, and commercially, were already on the stage. Ottmar Mergenthaler, the watchmaker from Württemberg, was working on his idea of the Linotype in Baltimore, and in Washington a civil servant who was also an amateur inventor was thinking out the details of what was to become the Monotype machine.

They were not, in their own day, however, seen to be indisputably the heirs of the future. Competing with them in their own fields, there were to be the Typograph, the Monoline, the Tachytype, and others, besides the typesetting machines using founders' type. The picture was confused.

MERGENTHALER
AND THE INVENTION
OF THE LINOTYPE

AMONG the numerous type-composing machines that claimed the attention of printers and publishers after the middle of the nineteenth century, many, despite repeated announcements, remained perpetually in a state of development, and many more never got further than the deposit of plans in the patent office. There was reason for the ironic comments and the scornful remarks that appeared in the various trade journals; irony and scorn which were not, however, free from a tinge of anxiety. If any of these many machines should at last prove to be successful—and some people knew that it could, after all, only be a matter of time—they would represent a serious threat to the living of armies of compositors. Composing rooms, especially those of newspapers, were large and full of equipment, and manned by rows of compositors. Each of these men stood at his case throughout the day, setting the type for the next edition, and after the paper was printed, that type had all to be distributed back into the cases again, ready for the next day.

Hand composition was a real bottleneck in the production of printed matter on a large scale, and there was no newspaper proprietor who was not ready to welcome with open arms a machine that would speed up composition. There was a fortune waiting for the first man to bring out such a machine. Everyone knew it, but no one could produce the goods.

Just after the mid-century, in 1854, there was born in Hachtel, a small town in Würtemberg, a child who was to alter all this in a manner so decisive as to change the world. Ottmar Mergenthaler was the third of a family of five children, the offspring of parents who were teachers, and who had themselves come of a line of schoolteachers. It was intended that Ottmar should also become a schoolteacher, and no doubt his education was designed with this end in view. At fourteen he was entered on the roll of a seminary, and it seemed that the die was cast for him. But he was not of the stuff of which schoolteachers are made. He had early showed an interest in mechanical things, in watches and clocks and their workings, in springs, gear trains, cams, and eccentrics. He must have delighted in taking these things to pieces and putting them together again. His interest in clocks was so well known in Hachtel that he was allowed to look after the village clock, and he kept it adjusted and in repair, renewing defective parts when this became necessary. The workings of any kind of machinery attracted him, and he liked to stand and watch it going, and to study what means had been used to overcome problems or to achieve particular ends.

The future of young Ottmar must have caused frequent discussion in the Mergenthaler household as it became increasingly evident that his interest lay elsewhere than in teaching. At last, the boy's father had to admit that some other career must be planned for him. It clearly had to be a career in mechanics. He was taken to Bietigheim, and there, in May 1868, at the age of fourteen years, he was apprenticed to a watchmaker named Hahl. The watchmaker undoubtedly found himself with an unusually enthusiastic and knowledgeable apprentice. Ottmar set himself to learn the work as quickly as possible, and at the same time he went to night schools to study mechanics and mechanical drawing.

He stayed with Hahl for four and a half years, and then, to better his prospects and perhaps to escape enlistment in the army, he decided to emigrate to America. His employer had a son in business in the United States, in Baltimore; there the son had a workshop for the manufacture of electric

X. THE SQUARE BASE LINOTYPE, REPRESENTING MERGENTHALER'S

FINAL VERSION, WITH A LINOTYPE SLUG

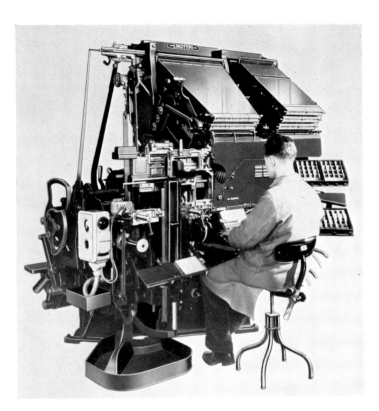

XI. A MODERN
LINOTYPE

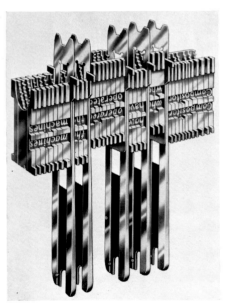

XII. A LINE OF MATRICES,
WITH SPACE BANDS

bells and signals, and it was there that Mergenthaler came to work, now rising eighteen years old.

He evidently worked well, and impressed the younger Hahl by his knowledge and ability, for three years later he was made foreman. He was now in charge of a workshop capable of producing experimental machinery as well as its ordinary run of work. It was about this time that he first came into contact with the problems of mechanical composition.

For some years a man of extraordinary tenacity had been investigating the field of mechanical composition, patiently seeking the means, and the man, to accomplish it successfully. James O. Clephane, who had served in the Lincoln government, had become interested in mechanical typesetting in relation to the proceedings of the courts of law. Not an inventor himself, he could nevertheless perceive a problem and then set himself to find the right man to solve it. When the man was found, Clephane found also the money needed to support the project. Two men, Densmore and Scholes, under his inspiration produced the first practical typewriter, which later became the Remington. But Clephane was after something that could do more than the typewriter could do. He wanted something that would produce a surface from which, somehow or other, printing might be done, so that the proceedings might then be printed without the intervention of hand composition at all.

It seemed possible to him that a machine might be made to produce an image or transfer or some such method from which a lithographic printing surface could be prepared, and Clephane secured the services of an engineer called Charles F. Moore to build such a machine for him. Moore went ahead and produced designs, from which he made a machine in 1877; but the lithographic image from it was poor and it was unsatisfactory.

Moore's machine was made in Hahl's workshop, and it was in connection with this that Clephane and Mergenthaler met for the first time in 1876.

Clephane's next idea was for a machine which, when its keyboard was operated, would cause raised characters, such as those on a typewriter, to make indentations in a *papier-mâché* sheet. This sheet would then be used to cast lines, and even pages, of type characters for use on the printing machine like a modern stereo. Mergenthaler seems to have seen disadvantages in this idea at once—and indeed, it was not a new idea, for it had been suggested long before, and even tried without success. The trouble with all such machines was simply the inconsistency in the size of the various characters of the alphabet. In any letterpress printing process, in which the characters are raised, the surface of all the characters of a page must present an even height to the paper on which it is to be printed. No letter may project above its fellows, none may be lower. If this condition is not observed, the printing will be defective because the letters that are high will press too heavily into the paper, while those that are too low may not print at all. This is familiar enough to any printer, who also knows that the tolerance above or below the correct height is small. In any such machine as that envisaged by Clephane, where the characters are struck individually into a *papier-mâché* surface, it would be essential that each character should bite into the surface to precisely the same depth. That cannot be achieved. The blow that will indent a w correctly will send a letter i much deeper, and a comma deeper still. No operator could be expected to achieve a touch so nicely differentiated, and an uneven printing surface must be inevitable.

Mergenthaler may have put such arguments to Clephane, but the latter was not convinced. He preferred to go away and put his new machine in hand in a workshop in Washington. There he worked for four years, with no result other than failure. But failure, repeated failure, did not damp Clephane's optimism or impair his persistence, or convince him that there was not somewhere a solution to the problem with which he had wrestled so long. He returned to Mergenthaler in Baltimore, and found in the clever young German new inspiration and new faith.

Perhaps Mergenthaler had thought about the matter during those four years Clephane had been away in Washington. If he had, he would have needed money to put any conception into practice. He certainly produced ideas now that Clephane was back and ready to find the capital that was needed. A company was formed to back yet another attempt at a composing machine, and Mergenthaler set to work.

His new machine was meant to indent characters into a *papier-mâché* flong just as the previous ones had done, but instead of indenting one character at a time, it was intended that a whole line should be indented at once. It was hoped that by this method a regular printing surface would be obtained and the disadvantages of the single-letter machines be avoided. In the event, this machine proved to be equally unsatisfactory, with new troubles of its own as well as some of the old ones.

There was nothing for it but to start again on some new tack, and in fact Mergenthaler's methodical mind had already worked out the new direction. He decided that it was quite useless to try to make a mould by indenting characters, either one at a time, or in a line: under the conditions of practical printing such an idea had no promise. It would be better, he thought, if instead of composing raised characters for indenting moulds from which to cast type, he arranged for movable moulds, or matrices, to be assembled, one for each letter, so that these might then be used to cast a line of type directly. The idea was original, and it seemed promising. Clephane and his friends, shouldering the loss on the first machine, were willing to back the new one. Work went ahead on it.

The result has come to be called the Band machine. It worked with a series of metal bars, or bands, each of which carried indented characters, or matrices, of the whole alphabet in one long line. When the operator pressed the keys of the machine, these bands were caused to move into position at a level corresponding to the key touched, so that the correct letter was presented for casting. One after the other the bands were alined according to the copy being set, and when the line was completed it was cast in front of a mould which formed the body or shank of the line.

Here at last was a machine that would work. Arrangements were made at once to put it on the market, so that

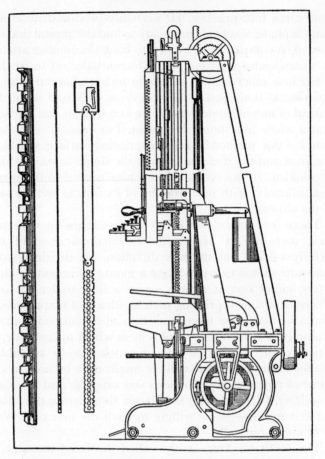

50. A diagram of Mergenthaler's band machine. The matrices were formed on bars, or bands, as shown at the left, and these were moved into position for casting by operating the keyboard.

some of the money sunk in the company might come back to it again and profits be earned. But Clephane reckoned without Mergenthaler. The inventor seemed now to make one machine merely to work out a newer and better idea. He came forward now with plans for an entirely different machine in which the matrices were not to be part of a band, but were to be independent and separate, held in magazines

168

and ready to be released at the touch of a key. Assembled into a line, they would be used to cast a line of type, and then they would be distributed back into their magazines again. In description it seemed to have many points of advantage, but there must have been earnest discussion among the members of the company. They might prefer to go ahead with the band machine, but if they did, then Mergenthaler might also go ahead with his better machine, and that might easily drive the earlier one from the market. Mergenthaler may not have been capable of bullying them in this manner, but it was clear that he was an inventor who must seek perfection, and it would be wise of the company, as businessmen, to take notice of the facts. They decided to support Mergenthaler in the construction of yet another machine.

It was ready in the middle of 1886. It had been awaited with considerable interest by the trade, and it was believed by many astute printers that here was the successful composing machine at last, that would break the bottleneck of the composing room and keep pace with the mechanization of the machine room. Newspapers were particularly interested in it, and several of the most important bought shares in the National Typographic Company of West Virginia, as Clephane's company was called. Among them were the *New York Tribune*, the *Washington Post*, the *Chicago Daily News*, and the Rand McNally Company.

The machine received its first commercial trial in the offices of the *Tribune*, under the eye of the newspaper's owner, Whitelaw Reid, who was a shareholder in the Clephane company. Mergenthaler, who by now, of course, knew very well the machine would work, must have felt a little nervous as he sat before the keyboard to cast the first lines; he knew as well as anyone else how temperamental any machine can be, especially when one is anxious to show it off. He had no need to worry. He tapped the keys and pushed the casting lever, and the cams and gears went smoothly into action; and a moment later, out of the bowels of the mass of complicated iron and steel a slight, gleaming slug of metal was thrust, to fall upon the galley placed to receive it. Whitelaw Reid pounced upon it at once, scanned the characters upon it, and cried: 'You have done it, Ottmar, you have done it, you have produced a line o' type.'

51. Mergenthaler demonstrates his 'Blower' machine to Whitelaw Reid in the office of the *New York Tribune.*

A name was needed for the new machine, and what could be more appropriate or illuminating than this? A Linotype it became, and Linotypes its successors remain to this day.

The company was confident that it had in its possession a truly efficient composing machine, and they had now to proceed to the successful exploitation of the invention. There was nothing in the way—nothing but the driving genius of Ottmar Mergenthaler. It seemed to him that his creation was still not perfect. The keyboard was not easy to operate, for it needed a lot of practice to make sure that only one matrix fell down at the touch of each key; a clumsy operator could cause the matrices to fall out of their channels in streams. Then, too, there was a blast of air, by which the matrices were carried to their position in the assembly slide in front of the operator, which was a nuisance because it blew dust and draught in the man's face all day. These faults could be cured, and in the curing of them Mergenthaler conceived yet another kind of Linotype, less cumbersome and more compact than the Blower.

He put his ideas to the board of the company, and no doubt he must once more have startled and dismayed them, but this time they would not yield. They were satisfied with the Blower, and they meant to put it on the market as a commercial proposition. It does not seem as though the gentlemen of the board and the inventor were at this time on the best of terms. Whitelaw Reid, it is said, wanted the workshops removed to New York, and Mergenthaler would not hear of this. These differences made Mergenthaler decide to leave the company. He sold his shares for $40,000, and went into business of his own account.

He was not entirely cut off from the company, however. He continued to manufacture the Blower machine for them, and he received royalties on the sales, as the inventor, but at the same time he went ahead with the construction of his new machine. It was a curious situation. He was earning money for manufacturing the Blower, and he was receiving royalties from it, while at the same time he was developing something that was to kill the Blower stone dead.

It took him three years to finish the project, three years of unremitting work—and he always worked hard—during which he was at times ill, and once seriously ill, but always

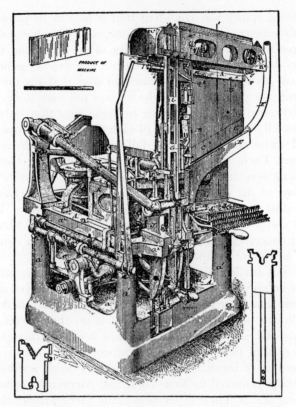

52. The 'Blower' Linotype, with a 'line o' type', a matrix,
and a space-band.

working. He worked on with a faith in his idea that was as
remarkable as the persistence of Clephane had been before.
He believed that he had the final answer, and he could not
help moving ahead to produce it.

The day came when he was able to announce that the new
machine was ready, and he invited his former colleagues of
the National Typographic Company to come and see it in
action. They did come, of course, and they had the sense to
see that Mergenthaler had made a machine as much in
advance of the Blower as the Blower had been in advance of
the Band. The matrices were released from their magazines

XIII. TOLBERT LANSTON

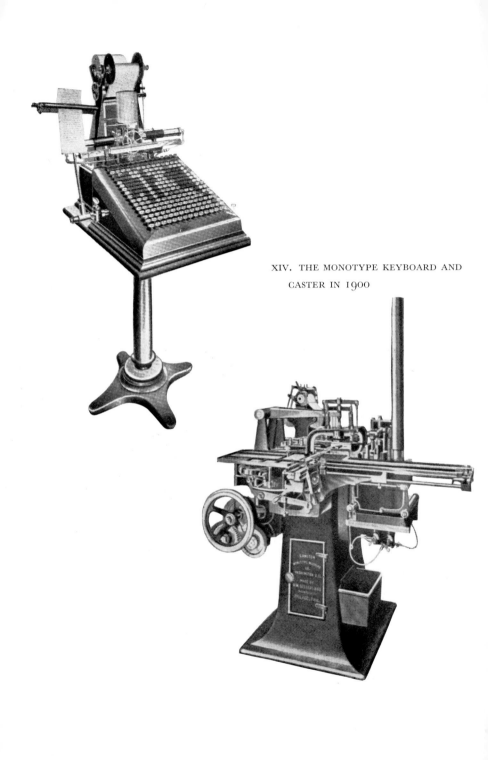

XIV. THE MONOTYPE KEYBOARD AND
CASTER IN 1900

smoothly and efficiently, and were delivered to the assembly slide by an endless belt. The visitors were so impressed that they invited Mergenthaler to join them again, on a new and presumably more advantageous contract. The new machine was at once put into commercial production.

As the various patterns and improvements of the Linotype were made, they had been submitted for patenting in the normal way, and patents were granted, so that the Linotype could not be copied. One patent, however, aroused an objection. One of the problems Mergenthaler had had to solve, like any other inventor of a composing machine, was the justification of the lines, the adjustment of the spaces between the words so that the lines should all be the same length. He adopted a system of double wedges, of which a pair were inserted after each word to represent a space of minimum width. When the line was complete the spaces could be widened by pushing the wedges together, when the line of matrices filled the measure. This device was submitted for patent, like any other, but now a hitch occurred. The patent office pointed out that a patent for a similar device had already been granted to J. W. Schuckers, of Philadelphia. Schuckers had built a line-indenting machine in 1881, but it had not been successful. He had then allowed his spacing device to be used by John Raphael Rogers, who had constructed another typesetting machine, the Typograph, in which the wedges were made circular in shape.

As soon as Schuckers realized that Mergenthaler was infringing his patent he set a legal action in motion to prevent him. Mergenthaler had previously proceeded against the Typograph company and had obtained injunctions against them. Philip T. Dodge, who had advised the Linotype company in other matters, and was one day to become its president, appeared for Mergenthaler and his colleagues. The action went on for some time, but the result does not seem to have been in doubt. Schuckers clearly held the patent, and the National Typographic Company was defeated and left with a problem on its hands the solution of which was urgently necessary for its continued existence.

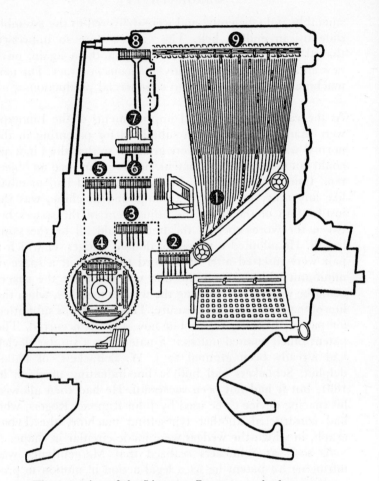

53. The operation of the Linotype. Pressure on the keys causes
matrices to fall as required from the magazine 1 to the assembly
slide 2, together with space-bands, which can be seen as the longer
items. The full line of matrices is carried through 3 to the mould
wheel 4, where it is clamped against a mould while molten metal
is injected. The slug, or line of type, is delivered to the galley below
the mould wheel. The matrices now start the return journey to the
magazine, from 5 to 6, where the space-bands are removed. The
matrices are lifted from 7 to 8, and they are then carried horizon-
tally across the mouths of the magazine, each matrix falling off
into its appropriate slide, ready for re-use.

Schuckers had hit upon what was the only sensible and practicable system of spacing in a slug-composing machine, and without the wedges the Linotype was useless.

On the other hand, the National Typographic Company held patents which prevented the Typograph company from carrying on with the manufacture of their machines. The picture of these two companies growling at each other, each from its own entrenchment of patents, is an amusing one, but the difference might easily have ended in the stifling of both companies and the loss of both machines—for both were practical, and both have survived.

There could be no solution but some kind of agreement between the two sides, and this in fact is what happened. The Linotype company was much the stronger, and they undoubtedly had the better of the two machines; but the Rogers company held the strategic patents on which the Linotype depended. There was nothing for it but for the Linotype company to buy out the Rogers company, and this they did, at a price—more than four hundred thousand dollars—which demonstrates the force of the Rogers position.

The purchase of the entire Rogers company, instead of simply the rights for the spacing wedges, while it may have been forced on Clephane and his friends, represented at the same time their desire to preserve a monopoly in the United States. Monopolies, however, can be expensive hobbies, and the Linotype soon found itself in conflict again. Rogers brought out a new Typograph, and one Wilbur Stephen Scudder designed a machine which he called the Monoline, which also cast a line of type in one piece, and which sold for a third of the price of the Linotype. In 1897 the Monoline was being offered at £320.

The Linotype company sent out a notice to the press to caution printers against using the Monoline, on the grounds that it infringed Linotype patents, and that the Linotype company were proceeding against the manufacturers. In the end the Linotype company had to buy out both Rogers and Scudder, but they were unable to prevent continued manufacture of the Monoline and the Typograph in Canada, where both machines seemed to do well—1,200 or more

Monolines were made in Montreal and sold in Australia, South Africa, and Latin America. This was too much for Clephane, and the Montreal company was bought out for $1,250,000. It seemed to have been the intention of the Linotype company to continue the manufacture of the Monoline by a subsidiary firm, but in fact the machine proved incapable of development. Scudder himself abandoned the principle, and went on to produce a Linotype kind of machine, the Intertype, which is now manufactured in the U.S.A. and in England. The Typograph, bought out or blocked by patents in the U.S., was taken to Germany and there it became popular.

In England a related company was making and developing the market for Linotypes, and it found itself in conflict in the same manner with other inventions. The Tachytype, for example, was a machine which was intended to set separate letters, which it cast from the directions of a perforated roll of paper something after the manner of the Monotype. This company seems to have been a thorn in the side of the English Linotype company. But a more serious opponent was on the way. The Monotype arrived in England in 1897. The Linotype directors were not impressed by it, or pretended that they were not; but just in case there was anything in this business of setting single types, they intended to be in it. They bought out the Tachytype and were ready.

A tremendous amount of money was now involved in the future of the Linotype. The investment of such huge sums showed confidence in the abilities of a typesetting machine of a kind that had never before been equalled. The machine was to justify the faith that the directors and shareholders of the manufacturing companies placed in it.

Mergenthaler, unlike so many other inventors, did very well out of the child of his invention. Royalties, and profits made out of manufacturing the Linotype, and his salary as a servant of the company, gave him a handsome income, and he was commonly reputed to be a millionaire. He was not to enjoy it for long, however. He had developed tuberculosis of the lungs some years before, after a bout of pneumonia which he had fought off while continuing to work, and now the disease had clearly become very serious. His doctors sent him to Saranak, where the purer air might do him good. He passed the time by writing his biography, only to have it destroyed in a fire, which also destroyed some of his property. This setback could not have helped him; but he fretted away from his workshops and the sound of iron, and in 1898 he returned to Baltimore, only slightly improved in health, and against the advice of his doctors.

A year later, at the age of forty-five, he died.

The Linotype was not the only fruit of Mergenthaler's inventive brain. He had turned his attention elsewhere at times, and among other things he invented a threshing machine and a basket-weaving machine. The Linotype, however, was much the greatest of his contributions to the welfare of nations, and it is by this machine, and only this, that he is remembered all over the world. Without others to inspire him—the indomitable optimism of Clephane, for example, whose part was not small, and the support of money, he could not have achieved what he did. Accident, or fate, brought together at last the men with the idea and the capital and the man with the ability to turn that idea into reality in the form of a thoroughly practical and immensely successful composing machine, the first that could be so described.

The results in the world have been plain. Without the Linotype there must have been far less printed matter, newspapers would have been smaller, books more expensive than they are, and probably even literacy less widespread than it is in the civilized nations today. And certainly there would have been less prosperity in the printing works, where the Linotype brought, not dismissal and poverty, as had been feared, and as indeed it did at first, but in the end prosperity and a vast increase in the extent of the trade and in the numbers employed in machine-room, composing room, binderies, and the many other departments of the printed word that depend, finally, on the issue of the bright slugs from the mould of the Linotype.

TOLBERT LANSTON
AND THE MONOTYPE

HERE are times when men who are trying to contrive a new invention of one kind or another find themselves stopped by a problem to which they can find no simple or practical solution; and then something comes to their notice that may have nothing at all to do with the subject, and the whole problem is illuminated as though at the click of a switch. Or the light may come on in the beginning and start a train of thought that ends eventually in a new kind of instrument or machine. There must have been such a flash, such an illumination of the way, when a modest civil servant, Tolbert Lanston, went to visit a friend of his, Colonel Seaton, in the Census Department of the U.S.A. in Washington. Seaton was trying out one of the new tabulating systems invented by Herbert Hollerith to deal automatically with various kinds of statistics and calculations, and he showed it off to Lanston. Seaton knew that his friend would be interested, for he was aware that Lanston counted himself a bit of an inventor too. In his spare time he had produced a new kind of mail-bag lock, and also an adjustable dumb-waiter, whatever that might be; and what is more significant to this story, an adding machine.

The Hollerith tabulator, the father of all modern tabulating machines, worked from a perforated card. Data from the census were translated into punch-holes in the card, and the card was then fed through a multiplying or tabulating machine which was controlled by electrical contacts operated by the punch-holes. The use of punched cards was not in itself new, or even the invention of Hollerith, for they had been used more than eighty years before, by Jacquard in revolutionary France, to control the pattern woven by his loom. Hollerith seems to have been the first to apply the system successfully to a mathematical purpose.

Lanston was certainly interested in the tabulating machine, which seemed to think for itself, and to multiply and tabulate at speeds far beyond the capacity of the cleverest of men. He must have studied it closely, either then or at subsequent visits.

Was he already thinking of a composing machine? There is nothing to tell us whether the idea was present in his mind at this early stage. It may, indeed, not have been his idea at all, but that of Seaton, who knew more about printing, and was more at home in the subject, than Lanston was. He was the son of a newspaper proprietor who had also been a contractor for government printing before the establishment of the U.S. government printing department. Seaton must have been well aware of the ferment that was going on at this time in the development of composing machines, which one after the other were brought to the attention of the printing trade, only to vanish eventually with their promise only partially fulfilled, or even as complete failures. There was no prime contender yet. Clephane and Mergenthaler were still struggling with the Linotype, and it was not yet on the market. Seaton knew of the need, and he also knew of his friend's inventive capacities. It is reasonable to think that it was he who first put the notion into Lanston's head, and he may also have suggested that the principle governing Hollerith's tabulator might also be used to govern a composing machine.

But how? There is a world of difference between a suggestion and a successful invention, a world of difference, days, years, of thought and experiment, and an essential seasoning of genius. Any such invention was going to involve a good deal more than a dumb-waiter or an adjustable horse-shoe—another of Lanston's inventions. And of course, the prize was greater. It was clear enough that there was a fortune waiting for the man who could produce a practical and successful composing machine. Lanston certainly took the idea seriously. If he thought that it was ambitious, perhaps too ambitious, for him, he did not let it worry him, any more than he allowed his comparative lack of engineering knowledge and experience to deter him.

Tolbert Lanston was not the kind of man to be easily deterred. Tenacious of his own ideas, even opinionated, he had a reputation, at least with his own family, for obstinacy and conviction. Persistence and intelligence had brought him from a poor family to a law degree and the management of his department in the civil service. He was born nearly forty years before the meeting with Seaton we are discussing, in Ohio, and there he was brought up, receiving an ordinary education until the age of fifteen. Then he had to go out to work to earn his living. Soon afterwards the Civil War broke out, and Lanston enlisted as a volunteer. He was twenty-one and a sergeant when the war ended. Then he was only one of crowds of men released by the rival armies, and all looking for work in a country torn and disturbed, and in which work of any kind was not easy to find. Lanston went to Washington and was successful in getting himself accepted as a clerk in the Pensions Bureau, which was busy trying to deal with the men who served or were injured in the war. While he held this job he began to study at the Columbian Law School, and he graduated there, to be admitted to the bar of the Supreme Court of the District of Columbia. In the meantime he made progress at the Pensions Bureau, and became in succession head of its four divisions, and eventually its chief clerk.

This is an unlikely career for a man who was to invent one of the most remarkable of machines. There is no hint of any kind of training in mechanics or engineering, no hint even of any deep interest in them, nothing to suggest that such a man might invent anything. His odd little inventions, like the mail-bag lock, the dumb-waiter, and the horseshoe appear to be nothing more than the productions of a dabbler with a logical and ingenious mind; but what about the adding machine? It would be interesting to know something more of this, for such a machine may be elaborate and intricate, and it is of particular interest because an adding mechanism is an essential part of the Monotype.

There is no doubt at all that Lanston did possess an ingenious and original mind. He was far better equipped for inventive thought than he was for practical engineering achievement, as events in the end proved. His ability and circumstances have some curious resemblances to those of Frederick Koenig, and if, like Koenig, he had had an Andre Bauer to depend on, the story of the Monotype might have been very different.

Lanston's thought on the development of a composing machine soon reached a stage at which experiment was necessary, and for experiment and the construction of a prototype, money was needed. He had not enough himself, but Seaton came to the rescue with financial assistance, and Lanston started to build his prototype.

It was ready for demonstration in 1887. It was really two machines, for Lanston had separated the operation of the keyboard from the manufacture of the type, a feature in which he differed from, for example, Mergenthaler, who, like most inventors, combined the two operations in one instrument. One of the two machines was the keyboard, with keys something like those of a typewriter, but not in the order of a modern typewriter or the modern Monotype. Pressure on the keys caused punches to rise and make perforations across the width of two rolls of paper, which were then moved on a step ready for the perforations for the next letter. The combination of punch-holes was different for every letter of the alphabet, so that when the copy had been set on the keyboard, the product was two strips of paper bearing the copy in the form of a code of punch-holes.

As the composition proceeded the width of the body of every character set was registered, and also the number of spaces between the words, and the result of the addition appeared against a pointer on a dial. With these figures, the operator was able to adjust the spacing, that is, to justify the line, by pressing the appropriate justifying keys.

The power needed to punch the paper ribbons came directly from the operator's fingers, and no light touch would do. The movement of the ribbons and of the calculating mechanism was achieved mechanically, the power

54. Lanston's first Monotype casting machine, a sprawling construction which worked.

coming from a falling weight on a chain. This weight had to be raised at the end of each line.

In a previous chapter I mentioned the difficulty of making a composing machine go back on its tracks to justify a line in the way that a compositor does. The idea presented no difficulty to Lanston. His division of the two operations of composing the type and manufacturing it made it easier for him. The second machine could logically start at the end of the composition and go on to the beginning, since this is the way the roll of paper from the keyboard would come to it: if you roll up a strip of paper, then the end of the strip is what you begin with when you start to unroll it. The first holes to be encountered would be the special justification holes at the end of the last line, and these set the spacing throughout that line, only to be changed by the presentation of the holes for the next line. The two strips of paper were loaded into the machine that made the type, and were unrolled in this manner across a series of electrical contacts—a concept borrowed directly from the Hollerith tabulator. These contacts allowed current through to operate the various components.

This machine did not cast type from molten metal, as a modern Monotype does. It had a matrix case containing 196 matrices or dies, and this was positioned by the contacts operated by the perforated holes. The machine was fed with a prepared strip of metal, and it cut sections of the strip as required for the width of the character to be made. Each section was held in a compression box while the die was brought down upon it with sufficient force to form the letter by pressure upon the cold metal. This description suggests that the method was essentially slow and crude, and it was soon clear that successful development could not lie along these lines.

The line of type was not justified by varying the amount of space between the words, after the manner of hand composition. Instead, an increment was added to the shank of each letter to drive the line out to the measure. In short measures, such a system must have given the appearance of letter-spacing in many lines. It was a very untypographical method, with objections on aesthetic grounds, and on grounds of practical legibility; but Lanston is not the only man who has thought that he could adapt typographical and literary customs to his machine, rather than adapt his machine to current usage.

Many of the fundamental principles of the modern Monotype are demonstrated in this prototype of Lanston's; but it had to be admitted that it was a failure. Nevertheless, it was a promising failure, and it seemed to Lanston and to others that it was necessary only to smooth out various difficulties and the thing was done. So it was, but it was by no means as easy as all that.

Lanston abandoned the idea of making type by compression of cold metal and set out to build a second machine which would cast type from molten metal. The matrix case was increased to hold 210 characters, and the electrical contact system was abandoned in favour of operation by compressed air. Most of his time and effort were concentrated on the improvement of the caster, as the type-manufacturing machine of the Monotype pair can now be called, for the keyboard seems to have given comparatively little trouble from the beginning. It remained as it was, with the power provided by the falling weight and the operator's fingers.

The caster did not prove satisfactory when it was ready, any more than the cold-compression machine had done. Certainly the caster set type, and set it very well, too, if one may judge from articles printed in contemporary journals which had been set on it. The caster was too slow, and it was not entirely reliable. No composing machine could be commercially successful that was not dependable, and which would not produce type at a speed considerably in advance of the best hand compositors.

Lanston proposed to increase the speed of the caster by multiplying the number of moulds to cast the body of the type, but this suggestion came to nothing, although some such machines were built and one with four moulds was exhibited at the World's Fair in Chicago in 1893. The Lanston Monotype machine seemed to be just another one of the many bright ideas of the kind that had come before the trade with great promise and had proved inadequate in performance.

These failures might have driven even a man of Lanston's self-confidence and persistence to despair. He had been trying for ten years now, and a lot of money of his own and Seaton's had been spent on the effort. If it had depended entirely on Lanston and Seaton, it is probable that at this stage, or earlier, the Monotype would have been abandoned as a failure, for neither of them could have found the money to go on indefinitely. They did go on because, perhaps through Seaton, Lanston had made the friendship of Harold Malcolm Duncan, a technical journalist and editor, and he, realizing the needs of the enterprise, which were simply capital to develop the invention until it could be made successful, introduced Lanston to J. Maury Dove. Dove was a prosperous merchant of, among other things, coal, and he was also an adventurous capitalist, willing to lay out and to risk his money. He was convinced of the value of the Monotype, and from that time forward he underwrote its development and provided the business brains and experience the inventor needed. A company, the Lanston Monotype Company, was formed, and Dove became its first president. He accepted the office with reluctance, for only six months, until a better man might be found; in fact he remained in office for over thirty years.

By this time it was clear that Lanston's Monotype was not going to be the first successful machine on the market. Mergenthaler's Blower might reasonably claim that honour, but by now the Blower had been superseded by Mergenthaler's new machine, and this was already in operation in many cities in the U.S.A. and in other parts of the world. It was a brave man who could consider setting up in competition with the proved and effective Linotype a machine that was still doubtfully efficient and was largely untried. J. Maury Dove was that man. He judged that the Monotype ought to be on the market, claiming its place in the sun. The company therefore had to find an engineering firm that could build the Monotype in quantity, and their choice fell upon a firm in Philadelphia, Sellers & Co. It was to prove a fortunate choice for the company, for they found in the Philadelphia organization not merely engineers who would be content to build machines as they were instructed, but a man who took a deep interest in the Monotype, who saw that the idea was good, but that the engineering could have been better.

A contract was placed with Sellers for fifty casters. The keyboards were to be built by a firm in Brooklyn, under Lanston's supervision. It was thought, when the order was placed, that the principal demand for the machines would be in the offices of newspapers, where a variety of text faces is not required. The new machines were therefore designed for only 132 characters instead of the 210 Lanston had allowed for in his second prototype. This restriction would appear, on the face of it, to be contrary to the trend of Lanston's intentions, and perhaps it was against his desire; but it was evidently designed to reduce the price and so increase the market. The machines were on sale in 1897, and they appear from contemporary accounts to have worked reasonably well, though the restricted range of the fount was not popular.

A second order for fifty machines was placed with Sellers. At this stage Lanston seems to have lost direct control, or at least complete control, of the development of his invention. It was probably inevitable. The company had to look to its best interests, and however brilliant Lanston's ideas might be, his colleagues had to depend finally on sound engineering practice to put those ideas into force to the best advantage. If Lanston had been, like Mergenthaler, himself a skilled engineer, the case might have been different, and the company that bears his name might also have borne a stronger impress of his personality. But Lanston was not a trained engineer. Practically all his experience of engineering was what he had gained in the development of the Monotype, and it filled his horizon too exclusively. And he was impatient of other people's advice. He was obstinate in preferring his own way, so his son says, and so far he had had his own way, at the cost of a great deal of money. It was time to bring other and more widely experienced minds to bear upon the problems of the Monotype.

In the Sellers organization a notable engineer, John Sellers Bancroft, took Lanston's caster in hand and drastically altered it. He reduced it in size, simplified it, increased its speed and accuracy, and in general made it recognizably the father of the modern machine. He extended the matrix case to hold 225 characters, in fifteen rows of fifteen characters each, and he dispensed with one of the two paper strips, so that the caster was controlled by a single strip, as it is today.

Bancroft also altered and improved the mechanism that controlled the movement of the matrix case. In Lanston's machine, the case, after being positioned for each character, returned to a base position, ready to go into action for the next letter. Bancroft applied to the movement a tongs arrangement that he had previously patented in connection with an apparatus for punching holes in boiler plate. This eliminated the necessity to return to base. 'Thus', his son Wilfrid Bancroft commented, 'the matrix case seems to have second sight, for after an "l", for example, is cast, if the next letter to be cast is another "l" the case remains as is and does not move at all.' More than this, in any instance the matrix case took the shortest route from letter to letter in Bancroft's caster, because of the tongs, and this improvement alone increased the speed of casting.

Bancroft also worked on the keyboard, and made a number of minor improvements. He retained the falling weight, however, to provide the power for the calculating mechanism. Bancroft's keyboard superseded the one developed by Lanston, but it was itself soon superseded by a new one designed by Lanston and made for him by a firm on Rhode Island. This competition between Lanston and Bancroft is a curious spectacle, and suggests that Lanston did not find as happy as he would have liked the collaboration in which he was nominally engaged with the firm that was making first casters and then keyboards for the company that was founded on his invention. He evidently thought it was more convenient and more satisfying to work alone.

Lanston's new keyboard was powered by compressed air, as the modern keyboard is. Connected to each of the 225 keys was an air valve, and when a key was pressed it opened its valve and allowed the air to pass to two of the punches in the paper tower, which rose and perforated the paper strip. The other movements of the keyboard, the line movement, the calculating mechanism, and so forth, were also powered by compressed air.

This new keyboard, the C keyboard, as it is known, held the field for some years, but once again it was Lanston's fate to show the way, to do the initial thinking, the inventive thinking, only to have the result bettered in practice by Bancroft. Bancroft's experience and knowledge enabled him, once the direction was indicated, to see more clearly than Lanston, to simplify and to improve, and to modernize. Bancroft's D keyboard, which was based on Lanston's, was also powered by compressed air, but the number of air valves was reduced drastically, from 225 to 33, and other improvements were made. The D keyboard is essentially the keyboard of today.

The Lanston company had not been enjoying plain sailing all this time. By 1897 it was clear that if some new and large access of capital were not forthcoming, the Monotype company and its machine would be in jeopardy. The expenses of developing the invention had passed beyond J. Maury Dove's capacity to finance them. Ten years had gone by since the machine had made its first appearance, fifteen or more since Lanston had begun on it, and the return to the men who had invested so much money and time and effort was disappointing. Worse, the machine at that time was still imperfect, and Bancroft was not satisfied with it. It was reckoned that a million dollars would be needed to develop and market it with any reasonable chance of success.

Where was so large a sum of money to come from? Certainly not from the present members of the company. The meeting at which this situation was discussed must have been despondent. Their one asset was the machine itself, but, whatever faith they might have had in it, it had not in fact been thoroughly tested by experience. There was little to suggest to printers that the Monotype was any better than any of the other machines of which they heard from time to time, or which, on occasion, they saw working under the hot-house conditions of an exhibition. Certainly, it could not be considered on the same level as the Linotype. True, the limited fount machine was on the market, and it had had some success. This was the only basis on which they could seek money, the only thing they had to offer. It was decided that examples of this machine should be taken to London, to see if money could be raised in what was then the hub of the world's finance. J. Maury Dove and Harold Duncan would go with them.

With four of the limited-fount machines packed up and stowed away, the two men sailed for England. It is not clear what exactly they intended to do, and probably they did not know themselves. No doubt they had introductions to in-fluential people, and they would set up their machines and operate them, and try to convince shrewd business men that here was a promising investment. The journey was vastly speculative, and perhaps because it was so the gods of chance were kind to them.

On board the ship the two Americans were introduced to the Earl of Dunraven, a world-famous yachtsman who proved himself a shrewd and far-seeing business man as well. They told him why they were going to England, and de-scribed their machine, and what it was meant to do and what they meant to do to develop it if they got the money they were after. Lord Dunraven was interested. He saw in Lanston's invention something that might well prove a worthwhile investment for himself and his friends, and an agreement was soon reached. As a result a Monotype was quickly erected and demonstrated when the travellers reached London. It so impressed the Earl and the friends he had brought in that they agreed to form a syndicate to buy the British rights for £220,000—the equivalent of the sum the American company had estimated it would need for its own purposes.

From this time forward, the progress of the Monotype keyboard and caster is divided between two independent companies. In America the Lanston Monotype Machine

Company took its million dollars and proceeded to build its factories, and in England the Lanston Monotype Corporation set out to establish the value of single-type composition in the face of the firmly established Linotype. The Linotype Company responded very quickly to the challenge. The various typesetting inventions of the period had made little impression against the general superiority of the Linotype, and the directors of that company meant to preserve their pre-eminence. The Monotype seemed to be a more dangerous competitor than some of the other machines, and it should, the Linotype directors decided, be combated on its own ground; for perhaps there was something in this business of single-type composition after all. The Linotype Company announced that it had bought the rights of a machine called the Tachytype, which, with a keyboard and a caster, set and cast single letters in justified lines in the same way as the Monotype did. The directors of the Linotype Company, it was announced, intended to find out 'whether genuine orders can be obtained for a machine built on the principles of the Lanston Monotype, and if there is any part of the printing field unoccupied, the directors intend to occupy it'. Perhaps it is a pity that the battle never amounted to much. The Tachytype, if it really worked as it was claimed to do, was a machine of excellent promise, and could claim in some ways to be superior to the Monotype; but it was found to infringe the patents held by the Monotype opposition and it has been heard of no more.

Dove returned in triumph to the United States and to his colleagues, leaving Duncan in England to help in establishing a factory here. His work done, Duncan then returned to the U.S., but he was soon recalled to become managing director of the English corporation.

As the business men took over and huge sums of money became involved, Lanston no doubt found himself more and more out of his depth, and his invention receding from him. There was little more for him to do. He had made his mark, produced his machine, and it was now in more capable hands than his for development. Some time after Bancroft's D keyboard appeared, it was announced that Lanston had discontinued his connection with the manufacturing side of the business and had assumed an advisory relationship. His part in the progress of the company after this was of only a minor nature, and for the remaining fourteen years of his life little was heard of him. He died in Washington on the 18th of February 1913.

INDEX

Aachen, pilgrimage to, 7
Addison, Joseph, works, 78
Adolf, archbishop of Mainz, 20
Amman, Jos, *Book of Trades*, 10
Andre and Senefelder, 102–3
Andre, Philip, 102–3
Anna of the Iron Gate, 5–6
Applegath, 137; and Cowper, 144
Ariosto, works, 85

Baltimore, 162, 164, 177
Bancroft, John Sellers, 187 sqq
Baskerville, John, 58, 114; origins, 59; education, 59; in Birmingham, 59; as writing master, 59; cutting gravestones, 60; and japanning, 60 sqq; house at Easy Hill, 61, 87; his dress, 61; and Sarah Eaves, 61–2; importance in Birmingham, 62; becomes printer, 62; portrait, 63; his press, 64; his ink, 65; manufacture of paper, 65–6; his types, 66, 72, 73; delays in production of books, 67–68; first book, 67, 68–9, 70–1; cost of printing, 70; Bible and Prayer Book, 70, 74, 75, 79, 83–4; his reputation, 71–3, 74, 80, 81; and Cambridge, 74; his aims as printer, 76; his staff, 77; his proof-reading, 78; his Greek type, 79; bereavements, 82; attempts to sell equipment, 83; and Robert Martin, 83; competition with Boden, 84; his will, 85–6; death, 85; removals of coffin, 87 sqq; attempts to rebury, 88–9; sale of foundry, 89
Bauer, Andre Frederick, 127, 136, 137, 139
Bavaria, 102, 104
Beaumarchais, 89
Bemberg, 1
Bensley, Thomas, 124 sqq, 136, 138, 139, 143
Bible, 36-line, 11, 12, 15, 20, 70, 74, 76, 77, 79, 80–4; 42-line, 15, 20, 57; Baskerville's, 74 sqq
Birmingham, 59–60, 61–2, 74, 82, 87
Blades, William, 32, 44
Blashoff, Peter, 1

Boden, 83–4
Bodoni, 58, 80
Book of Trades, 10
Bowyer, William, 48, 50, 51
Bruges, 32, 36, 39
Burgundy, Duke of, 31
Burgundy, Margaret, Duchess of, 31

Cambridge, University of, 57, 70, 74, 77, 80, 90
Canterbury Tales, 41–2
Caslon, William, 64, 67, 72, 73; and William Bowyer, 48; engraving guns, 48; in James's foundry, 48; in business as founder, 49; and Palmer, 49–50; his type, 50, 52–3; premises, 49, 50, 54–5; and music, 54; and William Ged, 56–7; his family, 58; death, 58
Catholicon, 20
Caxton, 76; in Low Countries, 30; appointed Governor of English Nation, 30; translation of *Recuyell*, 31; and Lady Margaret, Duchess of Burgundy, 31; in Cologne, 31; introduction to printing, 32; and Colard Mansion, 32 sqq; printing, Bruges, 32 sqq; his types, 32, 42–3; methods and equipment, 32, 34, 44; translations, 34; return to London, 35–6; as translater, printer, publisher, 37; market for his books, 37, 46; in Westminster, 38, 44; sign of the Red Pale, 39; his staff, 40; first book in England, 41; and *Canterbury Tales*, 41–4; his device, 45; death, 46
Chapter of St. Thomas, 11, 20
Chaucer, 37, 41
Chiswell Street, London, 51, 55
Clephane, James O., 165 sqq, 179
Cologne, 1, 31, 32
Cologne Chronicle, 9
Composing, hand, 154, 163
Composing machines, 143, 153 sqq, 162, 175, 176, 190
Compositors, 153, 159, 163
Convent of the Bare-footed Monks, 16, 17

193

INDEX

Day, John, 47
Deberny et Peignot, 89
Denmark, 80
Dictes and Sayings of the Philosophers,
41
Didot, 58, 86
Distributing machines, type, 158
Dodge, Philip T., 173
Dodsley, 67, 70, 71, 78, 82, 83
Donatus, 13
Donkin, Bryan, 117, 144
Dove, J. Maury, 185, 189, 190
Dritzehen, Andres, 6 sqq
Duncan, Harold Malcolm, 185, 190
Dunne, Hans, 7
Dunraven, Earl of, 189

Easy Hill, 61, 62, 74, 77, 82, 87, 89
Eaves, John, 82
Eaves, Richard, 61, 62
Eaves, Sarah, 61-2, 82, 89
Edward IV, of England, 39
Eltville, 20-1
English Nation, the, 30, 36
Engraving, 92-3

France, 82, 83
Franklin, Benjamin, 71, 73
Fust, Jacob, 13, 16
Fust, Johann, 13 sqq, 33

Game and Play of Chess, 34-5
Ged, William, 56, 145
Gensfleisch, Friele, 2
Gensfleisch (Gutenberg), 2
Gernsheim, Peter of, 16, 17, 20 (see
Schoeffer)
Gibson, and Baskerville's body, 87
Gleissner, 96
Gordon, and platen machine, 150-2
Greek classics, 77
Greifswald, 119-20
Grover's foundry, 48
Gutenberg, Johann, birth, 2; parents,
2; family, 2; inheritance, 3; other
names, 2; and clerk of Mainz, 3-4;
appearance, 5; breach of promise,
5-6; slander on Schotten Lawel, 6;
partnerships, 6-7; and manufacture
of mirrors, 7; and printing, 8;
and type mould, 8-11; and St.
Thomas's Chapter, 11, 13, 20;
World Judgement, 11; borrowing
in Mainz, 12, 13; 36-line Bible, 15;
42-line Bible, 15; astronomical
calendar, 13; Donatus grammar,
13; and Fust, 13 sqq; indulgences,
17; *Catholicon,* 20; retirement, 21;
and Dr. Konrad Humery, 21;

methods and equipment, 23 sqq;
his press, 25; death, 21

Hachtel, 164
Hanau, Bechtolf von, 16
Handel, 56
Hand-press, 106 sqq
Handy, John, 66
Hare, Bishop, 49-50
Heilmann, Andres, 6, 11
Helmasperger, Ulrich, 14, 16
Helmet Row, London, 49, 51, 54
Hoe, Richard, 146
Hoffmann, Johanna, 121-2, 141, 142
Hollerith, Herbert, 178, 179
Horace, 79, 85
Humery, Dr. Konrad, 21
Hunnemann, John, 124 sqq

Indulgences, 17 sqq
Ingoldstat, 91, 95
Ink balls, 27, 128-9
Ink, printing, 65
Ironmonger Row, London, 51

Jacobs, Fanny, 142
Jacquard loom, 179
James, Thomas, 56, 57; foundry, 48
Japan ware, 60, 61, 62, 65
Justification of type, 33, 44, 153,
155-7, 173, 181-4
Juvenal, 77

Keffer, Heinrich, 16
Kelheim stone, 93, 94, 96, 98
Koenig, Frederick, 154; hand-press
before, 106-17; his apprenticeship,
118-19; in University of Leipzig,
119; agreement with Riedel, 120;
first attempts to design machine,
118; and Johanna Hoffmann, 121-
2; first machine, 123-4; and
stereotyping, 122-3, 144; in London, 124, 143; appearance, 124; as
compositor, 124; and Thomas
Bensley, 124 sqq, 136; partners,
126; and John Walter, 125-6,
130 sqq; agreements, 125, 126-7;
and Bauer, 127; machine of 1810,
128; first cylinder machine, 129 sqq;
workshop in Whitecross Street, 132;
machines for *The Times,* 132; perfecting machine, 137; two-revolution press, 138; return to Germany,
139; at Oberzell, 179 sqq; marriage, 142; death, 143

Lanston Monotype Corporation, 190
Lanston Monotype Machine Company, 185

194

Lanston, Tolbert, and Colonel Seaton, 178; and Hollerith tabulator, 178–9; other inventions, 179; birth and education, 180; in Civil War, 180; as law student, 180; first machine, 181; method of justification, 181; second machine, 184; and H. M. Duncan, 185; and J. Maury Dove, 185; and J. Bancroft Sellers, 187 sqq; retirement, 190; death, 191

Latin classics, 77
Lawel, Schotten, 6, 14
Leipzig, University of, 119
Linotype, 162, 166 sqq, 179, 190
Lithography, 92 sqq; offset, 104
Livy, John, 82
London, 35, 37 sqq, 44, 70, 77, 78, 102, 124, 143, 189

Mädchenkenner, Die, 91
Mainz, 1 sqq; clerk of, 3–5; 12, 13, 31; Koenig in, 121
Mansion, Colard, 32 sqq
Marston, and Baskerville's body, 87, 88, 89
Martin, Robert, 83
Matrices, 22, 32, 167, 183, 187
Mercers' Company, 30, 46
Merchant Adventurers, 30
Mergenthaler, Ottmar, birth, 164; education, 164; apprenticeship, 164; in America, 164; and Clephane, 165 sqq; first machine, 165–6; line-indenting machine, 167; Band machine, 167–8; Blower machine, 169; and Whitelaw Reid, 169; leaves company, 171; and Schuckers, 173; patent rights, 174–6; his fortune, 176; death, 177; other inventions, 177
Metamorphoses, Ovid's, 36
Milton, works, 70, 74, 75, 76
Mirror of Salvation, 7
Mirrors, manufacture of, 7
Monotype Corporation, 90
Monotype machine, 155, 162, 176
Morison, Stanley, 90
Mould, type, 8, 22 sqq, 54

National Typographic Company of West Virginia, 169, 170, 173, 175
New York Tribune, 169
Nicholson, William, 116–18, 124, 144

Oberzell, 139 sqq
Offenbach, 102

Offset lithography, 104
Oxford University Press, 79, 89

Paige type-setting machine, 161
Palmer, printer, 49, 50, 51
Paradise Lost, 75
Pfister, Albrecht, 20
Prayer Book, 57, 70, 74, 76
Press, printing, Gutenberg's, 25–6, 126 sqq; Baskerville's, 64–5; Senefelder's, 97, 100, 101; hand, 106 sqq; bookbinder's, 106–7; first cylinder, 130; Koenig's, 118 sqq
Proof-reading, Baskerville's, 78
Punches, for type, 22 sqq, 32, 54

Quatres Dernières Choses, Les, 34

Red Pale, sign of the, 39
Reed, Talbot Baines, 85
Reid, Whitelaw, 169–70, 171
Riedel and Koenig, 120, 127
Riffe, Hans, 6, 11
Rivers, Earl, 41
Rogers, John Raphael, 173, 175
Rylands, John, 87, 88

St. Petersburg, 123–4
Schoeffer, Peter, 15, 17, 33
Schuckers, J. W., 173
Scudder, W. S., 175
Seaton, Colonel, 178 sqq
Sellers & Co., 185, 186
Senefelder, Alois, as an actor, 91; as playwright, 91; introduction to printing, 92; engraving and etching, 92–3; use of stone, 93–5, 99; as recruit to army, 95; becomes printer, 96; music printing, 96; his presses, 97, 98, 100, 101; discovery of lithographic process, 99–100; in Offenbach, 102; in London, 102–3; travels, 103; his book, 103; alternative printing surfaces, 104; death, 104
Senefelder, Peter, 91
Shakespeare, works, 83
Shenstone, William, 66–7, 78, 82
Sion Hill, Wolverley, 59
Society for Promotion of Christian Knowledge, 49, 51
Speculum Salutis, 7
Stanhope, Earl, 113–15, 145
Star Chamber, 47
Stephenson, Blake & Co, 51
Stereotyping, 56–7, 92, 142, 145
Strasburg, 1, 3, 6, 11
Suhl, 121, 122, 123, 124, 128

Taylor, Richard, 120, 143

Times, The, 126, 131–5, 138, 148, 159

Thüre, Ennelin zu der Iserin, 5

Tonson, 78

Troye, Recuyell of the Histories of, 28–31, 32, 33

Twain, Mark, 160–1

Type, first picture of casting of, 10; process of manufacture, 23, 24, 54; composing, 24–5; Baskerville's, 67; Baskerville's, Greek, 79, 89; Caslon's, 52–3; Caxton's, 42–3; supply to composing machines, 158

Typograph, 162, 173, 176

Virgil, works, 67, 68–9, 70, 71

Vitztum, Claus, 2, 5

Voltaire, works, 89

Walpole, 80

Walter, John, 125, 130, 131–5, 143

Warren, Thomas, 74, 79

Washington, 178, 180, 191

Westminster, 31, 38, 41, 44, 46

Wharfedale machine, 147

Wirich, Else, 2

Woodfall, George, 126

Worde, Wynkyn de, 32, 39, 40, 46

World Judgement, The, 11, 12

Zappe, Paul, 17

Zell, Ulrich, 31